6X

D1480940

VISUAL SPACE PERCEPTION

PALMER LIBRARY
CONNECTICUT COLLEGE

VISUAL SPACE PERCEPTION

by **WILLIAM H. ITTELSON, Ph.D.**
Associate Professor of Psychology, Brooklyn College

**SPRINGER PUBLISHING COMPANY, INC.
NEW YORK**

152.6
It 7

Copyright © 1960

SPRINGER PUBLISHING COMPANY, INC.

44 East 23rd Street   New York 10, N. Y.

Library of Congress Catalog Card Number: 60-15818

Printed in U.S.A.

To the Memory of

ADELBERT AMES, Jr.

198877

195877

Preface

In this book I have attempted to present a systematic statement of an approach to perception which has grown out of my work in that field over the past twelve years. Although I have devoted my efforts primarily to the study of visual space perception, and the experimental material in the book comes almost exclusively from that area, the theory of perception presented and its implications extend beyond that special topic. With this in mind, I have divided the book into three sections: first, a wide-ranging theory of perception, second, the core of empirical fact out of which the theory emerged, and third, some implications for special problem areas. To make the argument more rigorous and to indicate the way to quantitative tests at crucial points, the verbal statements have been supplemented, where possible, with simple mathematical derivations. Readers who are not professionally concerned with the experimental issues involved and who are primarily interested in obtaining an overall qualitative picture of the position set forth, may bypass the mathematical material without losing any of the essentials of the argument.

At various times and at various stages of the work, I have been assisted and deeply influenced by a number of friends and colleagues. My greatest personal and intellectual debt is to the late Adelbert Ames, Jr., who first crystallized my interest in the experimental study of perception.

In addition to the private appreciation which I have individually expressed, I would like to add a public record of thanks to Hadley Cantril, Silvan Tomkins, Carroll Pratt, Franklin P. Kilpatrick, Charles Slack, Edward Engel, Hans Toch and Samuel B. Kutash. Without their friendship, encouragement and assistance this book could never have been written.

The research on which the book is based has been supported by a number of organizations who have been generous in providing funds and encouragement. The Rockefeller Foundation, The Office of Naval Research, The National Institutes of Health and the Veterans Administration have all provided assistance at one time or another. The actual preparation of the manuscript was made possible in part by a sabbatical leave from Princeton University, in part by a Social Science Research Council grant-in-aid and in part by released time from Brooklyn College. For all of this help and for the implied confidence it represents, I am indeed grateful.

The writing of the book has progressed gradually over a period of years. During this time some of the material has, in substance, been made available to investigators. In much briefer and modified form, Chapters II and III appeared as *Perception: a transactional approach* by Ittelson and Cantril (Copyright 1954 by Random House, Inc.). The basic approach to the invariance hypothesis, which runs through much of Part Two, was originally worked out and published as Kilpatrick and Ittelson, The size-distance invariance hypothesis, *Psychological Review*, 1953; a portion of this paper is used in Chapter IV. The material dealing with person perception, Chapter X, was published in similar form as Ittelson and Slack, The perception of persons as visual objects, in *Person perception and interpersonal behavior*, edited by Tagiuri and Pertrullo, Stanford University Press, 1958. Part of Chapter VIII, dealing with accommodation and convergence, originally appeared as Ittelson and Ames, Accommodation, convergence and their relation to apparent distance, *Journal of Psychology*, 1950. I appreciate the permission granted to use and modify this material.

William H. Ittelson
Brooklyn, N.Y.
July, 1960

Contents

Contents

Part One

THEORY OF PERCEPTION

I

Introduction

The past fifty years have seen an intellectual revolution in all areas of human understanding. In the field of perception this has been reflected by making the dependence on perceptual theory explicit in studies in which previously the relationship had been only vaguely seen or intuitively felt. No matter how peripheral or how implicit this connection may have been, however, the entire history of human thought is interwoven with the history of thinking about perception. No matter how limited and concrete the problem of the contemporary theorist, there is always stretching out behind him and at least on the periphery of his awareness a vast body of accumulated wisdom and observations.

The long development of speculation about perception in philosophy, continuing to the present day, is well known, as is its outgrowth, a century ago, of the beginnings of experimental psychology. Today the importance of perception as a key psychological process is being stressed from many directions. Experimental psychology—starting with the Wurzburg work, then Gestalt, and today on many fronts—has shown the problem to be complex and related to many other psychological processes. Projective techniques have shown that perception mirrors many conditions which previously had been considered independent processes. Psychoanalytic theory and personality theories growing from it can also be cited as stimulating and making explicit an interest in perception.

The impact of perception theory on philosophy and psychology, important though it is and central to this book, nevertheless does not exhaust the points of contact between the study of perception and other human activities. Indeed, the impact of the rational and intellectual aspect of perception can be matched by an equally fascinating and important inter-relationship with man's aesthetic experiences. The mutual interdependence of art and perception can be seen, on the one hand, in the creative process of representing and communicating perceptual material, and on the other in the aesthetic experience involved in the perception of a work of art. It is of interest that, on the evidence of cave drawings and other examples of prehistoric art, the visual space cues which are still subjects of study today were at least implicitly and intuitively dealt with by earliest man. With the early perspectivists and then Leonardo, the interdependence of pictorial art and perceptual theory became explicit. Similarly, the production of artifacts or architectural structures always demands a theory of perception which may be the crudest kind of implicitly held realism, but frequently becomes quite sophisticated and explicit. In art and architecture today a growing number of contemporary writings make quite explicit a dependence on perceptual theory and not infrequently expound views far removed from those of writers in other fields.

A third line of human endeavor greatly influenced by and dependent upon perceptual theory is the development of science. It is a fundamental principle that scientific method rests on observable phenomena. Since science rests on observation, problems of perception have always been explicit or implicit in science. Indeed, in science perhaps more than any other sphere during the last fifty years the whole concept of observation has come in for renewed study, epitomized by Bridgman and the interest in the operational approach.

Wherever one looks, to rational, aesthetic or scientific man, one finds perception standing as a key concept. Perhaps it will be thought presumptuous to offer to introduce the reader to a subject with which he is already so familiar. Indeed, everyone of us perceives, and each of us has through his life's experiences developed a profound understanding based on a vast accumulation of evidence, on repeated and verified observations. And yet this very fact that each of us has already arrived at his own understanding of what perception is makes it imperative that we start with defining, however broadly, what it is we are investigating. Certainly the first step in any inquiry is to delimit the area of study and to mark out the subject matter. This preliminary task is important both to keep us from bypassing problems that properly belong within our study and to help us avoid questions that are actually outside of it. Since perception can never be a novel topic, it is well to be cautious in avoiding at the outset the misunderstandings that stem from differing preconceptions.

If one looks at the question of defining the subject matter of perception from the standpoint of one's own experience, it seems at first glance to be simplicity indeed. We all perceive, and we all know what we mean when we say we perceive; the question of differentiating perceiving from other psychological activities does not seem to offer any obstacles. The differences between perception and such processes as judgment, memory, and knowledge, for example, seem striking and adequately determined by common sense. As I look up from my desk I cannot avoid seeing a wooden chair against the opposite wall, and it certainly seems obvious to me that my perception of that chair is unequivocably differentiated from such other aspects of my experience as my memory of another chair, my judgment that this particular chair is over 100 years old, my knowledge that it belongs to me, my feeling that it is a very beautiful chair indeed, and my prediction that unless some glue is applied it will very shortly cease to be a chair at all.

Unfortunately, however, to the man in the laboratory those distinctions are not always so clear nor so sharp. We can ask some questions which may point out the difficulties. Do the distant mountains look twenty miles away? Or do they look some indeterminate distance, and, because they look thus and so, I judge that they are twenty miles away? How big does the moon look? Most people make an estimate of about the size of a dinner plate. But in what sense does the moon appear dinner-plate size? Certainly not in the same sense that the plate itself does. An apple looks red, or do we remember that apples are red? The floor looks hard, or do we know that it is hard? A Rembrandt or a Picasso looks beautiful, or do we simply see a mass of light and dark, color and shadow, and add the experience of beauty as something quite separate from that of perceiving?

These examples have not been chosen at random. Every one of them has a history of experimentation and speculation behind it. Taken together, they serve to illustrate the fact that upon close examination a straight-forward, commonsense definition of the subject matter of perception is not easily obtainable. While we may think we know what we mean by perception we quickly find that the drawing of sharp lines about certain aspects of experience and stating "inside this area is perception and outside of it not" is a difficult if not fruitless task.

An appraisal of one's own experience then, fails to reveal any clearcut answer to the question of what we are talking about when we talk about perception. But when we leave our own personal experience and seek an answer by referring to what has been written by others on the subject, our confusion becomes worse. Far from having no answer we find ourselves faced with a multiplicity of answers. We can in desperation turn to the dictionary and learn that perception is "the awareness of objects." But this helps us little when we realize that we would have to search long today to find a psychologist or a philosopher who would assert that when he talks about perception he is talking about the awareness of objects and nothing more.

Men have been writing about perception for millennia, but there is still no general agreement between authors as to what it is they are writing about. Those who accept disagreement among philosophers as the rule are sometimes surprised to learn that even experimental psychologists offer almost as many definitions of perception as there are experimenters; even within the context of scientific psychology it cannot be assumed that the reader will have a clear and unequivocable understanding of what an author refers to when using the term "perception."

We are faced, then, with the paradox that one of the oldest studies within scientific psychology yet remains without a formally accepted definition. On closer examination it may be that the very fact of the venerability of perception accounts for the lack of definition. Psychology has in its history passed through many phases of emphasis, has had its ardent proponents of divergent schools, has defined its subject matter in a variety of ways. And as psychology itself has grown and changed, so has the way it has posed the problem of perception. In this sense, the many definitions of perception are merely reflections of the many facets of psychology.

A glance at two typical issues may serve to illustrate this point. Does perception always involve conscious awareness or can the term be applied to unconscious processes as well? Even a passing familiarity with the history of psychology shows that the question of conscious vs. unconscious processes is not limited to problems of perception but represents an old and continuing issue cutting across all areas of psychology. Or again, does the external stimulus determine perception or must "inner" factors be taken into account? Clearly, the question of limiting our study to responses to external stimuli transcends the study of perception; it symbolizes two contrasting approaches to the entire subject matter of psychology.

Perhaps every approach to psychological theory has been reflected in its own definition of perception. Similarly, it is not surprising to find that a diversity of ways of defining the subject matter has resulted in diverse ways of formulating the problem of the study of perception; there are as many different problematizations as there are different definitions. Nevertheless, without doing too much violence to the many views represented, one can indicate three general approaches, each of which has some degree of historical continuity and coherence, and each of which has tended to formulate its problems in such a way as to deny or do violence to the problems of the other two. These three contrasting views are the phenomenological, the stimulus-response and the functional. Today one rarely encounters any one of these in pure form, and perhaps they are best considered as elements that appear to greater or lesser degrees and in varying combinations in most current definitions of perception.

The phenomenological approach attempts to define perception in terms of the subjective experience of the perceiver. The stimulus-response approach, in sharp distinction, attempts to define perception in terms of observable characteristics of the stimulus and the response. These two contrasting definitions grow out of two different philosophical ways of thinking, each with deep historical roots. The first mode is that of the "idealist" who concentrates on the thoughts and feelings of his own experience. The second represents the "realist" who is concerned with the observable objects and events of the external world. The *reductio ad absurdum* of the first view is reached by the solipsist, who believes that there is nothing outside of his own head, of the latter view by the behaviorist, who believes that there is nothing inside of his.

A functional definition tries to bridge the gap between these divergent views by specifying the perceptual process in terms of the relationship of that particular process to the total life functioning of the individual. A functional approach is by its very nature future-oriented and goal-directed. Its chief advantage derives from this very fact. A functional definition puts the person into a real situation and considers him as he actually appears in concrete living. Without in any way denying the importance of the long traditions of thought underlying the phenomenological and behavioral points of view, this book will be devoted to the elaboration of a functional approach to perception.

Perceptual studies initiated the modern era of scientific psychology. A look at the course of development of the study of perception since that time gives us a bird's-eye view of the development of the entire field of psychology, and indicates why a functional approach to perception has become imperative in the climate of contemporary psychology. The early perceptual work fell within what has come to be known as the tradition of stimulus determination: the view that the external stimulus determines the perception. Emphasis was placed on a detailed analysis of the characteristics of the external stimulus, and the search was for universal "laws" relating the physical environment and the subjective experience. Within the limits of this approach it was gradually found necessary to enlarge the subject matter to include the study of the sensory apparatus and of neural processes and central functioning as well. This line of approach has been and continues to be actively pursued and productive of important findings.

Within the past decade or so, however, the experimental study of perception has received a tremendous impetus from a point of view almost directly opposed to this. The early work started with the object and went to the person. It asked: "What does the environment do to the perceiver?" Present day thinking reverses this, starts with the perceiver and works toward the object. Today we ask: "What does the perceiver do to the environment? What is actually done by the individual when he perceives?" The revolutionary shift, then, is from considering perception as a passive reaction to external events toward considering perceiving as a process actively carried out by the perceiver.

In short, the over-all trend of contemporary perceptual studies has been away from the stimulus orientation and toward the treatment of perceiving as an essentially creative process actively carried on by the organism. The assumption is that the individual acts in any situation in terms of the way he perceives that situation. Perception, then, becomes a crucial process intimately involved in the effective functioning of the individual. Such an approach has necessarily led the experimental study of perception into a consideration of problems which had previously been considered a sacred domain of that branch of psychology labeled "personality."

Actually the meeting has been at the half-way mark. More and more, personality theorists and practicing clinicians have become interested in the perceptual process, and an analogous trend can be traced from their starting point. Certainly the most fruitful clinical approaches currently in use in psychodiagnosis and psychotherapy rely on a theoretical basis which assumes a relationship between perception and personality. Psychoanalysis, of course, has always assumed that the individual structures his world through his experiences. The direct importance of perceptual processes in shaping the content of these experiences is specifically stressed by most contemporary psychoanalytic writers. The relationship of perception to phenomenological personality theory is even more direct. The projective theorists have always maintained this position, and in a sense are today coming into their own. Rorschach himself referred to his test as an "experiment in perception." It is safe to say that personality studies have been approaching perception as rapidly as perceptual studies have been approaching personality. The two have met with an impact that is vitally affecting psychology.

Today's changing emphases serve to underline the fact that the study of perception is a very old one, with roots in a wide variety of human activities and experiences—social, aesthetic, philosophical, scientific. In all these areas it has received an impetus that represents more than an acceleration of the age-old studies. It is, rather, a push in a radically new direction. Contemporary thinking in all these fields has, at the very least, elements of intellectual revolution and radical departure from earlier views.

Within scientific psychology, the central and dominant position currently held by perception can be attributed to two compelling reasons. First, considered as a subject matter for study within the science of psychology, perception represents the common meeting ground between the tradition of experimental psychology on the one hand and that of clinical practice on the other. Perception becomes a central unifying study linking the laboratory with the clinic.

Second, considered as a psychological process, perception occupies a central, unifying position within the total functioning of the individual. If we may permit ourselves for the moment the simplifying assumption of a dichotomy between the individual and the environment, the reason for this importance of perceiving becomes obvious. It is through perception that each one of us becomes aware of the world outside of himself.

Of course, intercourse between the individual and his environment is a two-way affair, involving both incoming and outgoing channels. These are most adequately conceptualized, respectively, as perceiving and acting. Any adequate theory must account for both of these processes, and it may appear on the surface that an emphasis on perception leaves out action and hence is limited to only half the problem, and possibly the less important half. However, the error of this view becomes apparent from a closer look at the relationship between perceiving and acting. In dealing with the world about him, each person necessarily acts in terms of the world as he perceives it. He has no alternative, for that is the only world he lives in, the only world he experiences. As Ames so well put it, perceptions are prognostic directives for action.

Actions are not only initiated, they also have consequences. They have an effect, first, on the object of the action. This is their outgoing aspect. But from a psychological point of view, the most important effect of acting is on the person who initiated the action —the way he himself experiences the consequences of his own actions. And this, in turn, is accomplished through the perceptual process. Perceiving, then, provides both the framework on which action is based and the channel through which the consequences of action are experienced. Considered either as a subject matter for study or as a psychological process, perception offers an important meeting point for many and varied areas of psychology, a point from which one can travel in many directions.

II

What is Perception?

The term "perception" labels a subject matter for inquiry which at the present time does not possess a definition that can be clearly stated or agreed upon. It seems appropriate to ask ourselves the simple question, "What is perception?" In one sense, the entire book is devoted to answering this question. In a more restricted sense, this chapter aims at a provisional answer from which the rest of the study can proceed.

As a point of departure, we can note that most writers state, explicitly or implicitly, that the function of perception is to bring us into contact with the world outside of ourselves. Furthermore, it is usually stated that this contact is through our senses—that the only things we can know about the world come to us through the medium of our sense organs. This view of perception as organized about the sense modalities is, as we shall see, not adequate in the light of present day knowledge but provides the historic background for the study of perception. It is this sensory orientation of perceptual study that has invited such phrases as William James' "blooming, buzzing confusion" of the infant's world and Einstein's "rabble of the senses."

In this book we will approach perception from a functional rather than a sensory point of view, with a concurrent emphasis on psychological rather than physiological variables. This is in no way intended to imply that the physiological study of the sensory organs is not an important part of perception but rather to indicate that it is one of the important areas of study which we are omitting.

While we will primarily be concerned with human visual space perception, brief mention, at the outset, of some of the sensory processes in the lower organisms will help us bear in mind the continuity of human behavior with that of the lower animals. All organisms can be said to perceive. Even unicellular microorganisms demonstrate differential sensitivity to environmental conditions. Perception in higher organisms is, however, qualitatively quite different from this type of gross discrimination. Physiologically, this difference is due primarily to the greater specialization of sensory nerve endings and the elaboration of cerebral centers. From an evolutionary standpoint, the most interesting development from the lower organisms to the higher is the appearance in all higher animals of so-called distance receptors, primarily eyes and ears, which in a sense liberate the organism from complete dependence on the state of things adjacent to its bodily surfaces, and enable it to deal with distant environmental happenings.

The statement that we will be concerned with human *visual* space perception is in the classical tradition that started with the Greeks. However, the familiar five senses—sight and hearing, touch, taste and smell—have lost scientific status with the discovery in some animals of special sensitivities, for example, thermal sensitivity; with the recognition of sensitivity to internal bodily conditions, for example, hunger and muscular states; and with the extension of perception in man to include complex psychological activities, such as the perception of emotions in others. Today, while classification in terms of senses is still common, so many different and overlapping sensations have been explored that such classification is of little value other than descriptive.

Any attempt to classify perception in terms of *function* rather than sense modality would involve extreme overlap between the various modalities. While no such classification of perception will be attempted here, some of the implications of such reorganization can be indicated if we consider the functions of two of the traditional modalities, vision and audition. Broadly speaking, the two major functions served here are those of spatial orientation and abstract communication. While visual space perception is undoubtedly the more important, auditory space perception plays a large role in human behavior and a dominant role in the spatial orientation of some lower forms. Visual and auditory space perception, therefore, cannot adequately be considered as separate subjects but should be studied as they actually function in complex interaction not only with each other but with many of the other sense modalities.

Except in man, abstract communication is largely limited to audition. In the lower animals, communication consists primarily of warnings. In higher animals, in addition to warnings, there are identifications, mating calls, etc. In man, vision and audition share the function of providing intellectual and aesthetic communication through language and various other abstract forms—a function which is in all other organisms either very minor or non-existent. This is good evidence for believing that in many ways perception in man is quite different from that in animals. Nevertheless, no such sharp distinction is evident in the peripheral physiology of man and that of other animals.

Similarly, when we compare the brain of man with that of lower animals we find that there is no clear-cut qualitative difference although there is a definite progression from the lower animals on up to man. In contrast with the continuity in physiological structure, many capacities are in man qualitatively quite different, such as abstract thought and communication, which appear in other animals in only a primitive way. Undoubtedly these differences are due in some as yet unknown way to the greater complexity of the nervous system of man. This same complexity undoubtedly accounts also for the differences between human perception and that of lower organisms which are not directly traced to receptor differences. We do not study abstract thought or aesthetic appreciation in animals nor can we properly study human perception in animals. Similarly, many of the conclusions about perception in man at which we will arrive need not and probably do not apply to any other organisms.

THE MAJOR CHARACTERISTICS OF PERCEPTION

There are three features of perception which deserve special attention with respect to human perception. Taken together, these features delimit the subject matter of perception and will lead us to a statement of the problem of perception. First, the facts of perception always present themselves through concrete individuals dealing with concrete situations, and may be studied only in terms of the *transactions* in which they can be observed. Second, within such transactions, perceiving is done by a particular person from his own position in space and time and with his own combination of experiences and needs. Perception enters into the transaction from the unique *personal behavioral center* of the perceiving individual. And third, within the particular transaction and operating from his own personal behavioral center, each of us through perceiving creates for himself his own psychological environment by attributing certain aspects of his experience to an environment which he believes exists independent of the experience. This characteristic of perception we can label *externalization*.

PERCEPTION AS TRANSACTION

In man, perceiving is not only an inseparable part of all waking activity but, even more important, perceiving never occurs independent of some other activity. To attempt to find examples of waking activity not involving perception, one is forced to go to Yogi practices and trance states in which the person attempts to maintain conscious thought while completely removed from all contact with the environment through perception. There is some evidence that some people may be able to achieve this condition. Even if fully established, such instances are certainly so rare that we will not consider them as disproving the general rule that waking activity always involves perception.

In an effort to find examples of perception independent of other human activity we look not to advanced mysticism but to budding science. The introspectionism of early experimental psychology had as one of its fundamental tenets the belief that one could, in fact, observe one's self perceive without reference to any other activity. Unavoidably, this statement contains circularity, and this aspect of early experimental psychology has not been fruitful nor carried on to the present time. Certainly, reference to one's own experiences indicates that perceiving and other activities are inextricably interwoven.

But how are we to study perceiving if we can never find a perception? The answer is that perceiving is an abstraction from a concrete experience and must be treated as such. We cannot somehow isolate a perception in its "pure" state as a chemist can isolate a pure chemical or a biologist a pure strain, and then proceed to study perception in isolation. Perceiving never takes place "by itself." It can only be studied as part of the situation in which it operates.

For purposes of experimentation, the abstraction of some simple act of perceiving from the rest of an on-going situation is frequently necessary, but it always involves the risk of seriously distorting the subject matter. The starting point for perceptual studies must be perceiving as it is encountered in concrete, real-life situations. This places severe restrictions upon the experimental study of perception and has methodological and procedural as well as theoretical implications. No matter how much he may wish to do otherwise, the student of perception is frequently forced to obtain data under conditions quite remote from those in which perception normally operates. When he does so, he must be sensitive to the limitations of treating such data as if they had relevance to real-life situations. The safe way out of this difficulty is to treat an experiment in the perceptual laboratory not as a reflection of how one perceives in another kind of situation but as a concrete situation in itself in which the observer is perceiving.

Neither a perception nor an object-as-perceived exists independent of the total life situation of which both perception and object are a part. It is meaningless to speak of either as existing apart from the situation in which it is encountered. The word *transaction* is used to label such a situation, for the word carries the double implication (1) that all parts of the situation enter into it as active participants, and (2) that they owe their very existence as encountered in the situation to this active participation, and do not appear as already existing entities that merely interact with each other without affecting their own identity.

The term *transaction* was first used in this general context by Dewey and Bentley for whom it took on far-reaching philosophical significance. What they mean by this term can best be gathered by their own words. "Observation of this general (transactional) type sees man-in-action not as something radically set over against an environing world nor yet as merely action 'in' a world but is action of and by the world in which the man belongs as an integral constituent." Under this procedure all of man's behavior "including his most advanced knowings" are treated as "activities not of himself alone nor even as primarily his but as processes of the full situation of organism-environment." "From birth to death every human being is a *party* so that neither he nor anything done or suffered can possibly be understood when it is separated from the fact of participation in an extensive body of transactions—to which a given human being may contribute and which he modifies but only in virtue of being a partaker in them."

Dewey and Bentley distinguish this transactional procedure from two other procedures which they feel have largely dominated the history of science up till now. First came what they call the antique view of "self action where things are viewed as acting under their own powers." Second is the interaction view of classical mechanics "where thing is balanced against thing in causal inter- connection." In transactional observation "systems of description and naming are employed to deal with aspects and phases of action without final attribution to 'elements' or other presumptively de- tachable or independent 'entities,' 'essences,' or 'realities' and with- out isolation of presumptively detachable 'relations' from such detachable 'elements.' "

Speaking more specifically of visual perception, Bentley said, "We do not, however, take the organism and environment as if we could know about them separately in advance of our special inquiry but we take their interaction itself as subject matter of study. We name this *transaction* to differentiate it from interaction. We inspect the thing-seen not as the operation of an organism upon an environment nor of the environment on an organism but as itself an event." This point of view is in many ways foreign to our common sense view of things. We tend to look at the objects and people around us as entities existing in their own right and quite independent of our transactions with them. As we shall see, this common sense view is necessary for us if we are to carry on our daily activities and is itself one of the products of the process of perception. But this common sense view is not adequate for scien- tific understanding.

PERCEPTION AS UNIQUE

Just as no single aspect of the transaction can be said to exist in its own right apart from the transaction, so not even the trans- action itself can be treated as existing in its own right. Using the term transaction is not to be construed as simply a new way of breaking the subject matter into larger but still discrete elements or events. This view, which we will avoid in this discussion, is analogous to the view of Newtonian physics in which the belief was held that the observer somehow stood outside of the system that he was observing and which was independent of the fact of observation. Rather, we will assume that every transaction has within it as an integral part of its being its own unique reflection of all past transactions and its own unique presentment of future transactions.

"An event has contemporaries," to use Whitehead's terms. "This means that an event mirrors within itself the modes of its contemporaries as a display of immediate achievement. An event has a past. This means that an event mirrors within itself the modes of its predecessors as memories which are fused into its own content. An event has a future. This means that an event mirrors within itself such aspects as the future throws back on to the present; or, in other words, as the present has determined concerning the future. . . . These conclusions are essential for any form of realism for there is in the world for our cognizance memory of the past, immediacy of realization and indication of things to come."

Even the scientist studying the transaction enters into it as a participant. He does not stand outside it, he does not observe it from some remote and inaccessible position. The very fact of observation has been shown in the physical sciences to affect that which is observed. How much more obvious this becomes in the behavioral sciences. The psychologist is always a participant who affects and is affected by the transaction he is "observing."

The fact that a transaction does not exist in its own right waiting for observation but rather can be observed only through participation has one very important implication for our present discussion. Each participant enters into the transaction in a different manner and the transaction he experiences is to this extent different from that experienced by all other participants. There are as many points from which the transaction can be entered as there are participants. Each participant observes and acts from his own *personal behavioral center*. Perceiving is always an activity by a unique participant from his unique position providing him with his unique world of experience. The term "personal behavioral center" carries this threefold connotation. Experiences are "personal" and unique. No two people can enter into the transaction in exactly the same way. "Behavioral" implies active participation as opposed to passive observation. "Center" implies that participation occurs from one point and from that point alone. Any aspect of the transaction that cannot be reached, or in Whitehead's term "mirrored," from that point is unknown. In Whitehead's words, "No statement, except one, can be made respecting any remote occasion which enters into no relationship with the immediate occasion. . . . The one excepted statement is:—If anything out of relationship, then complete ignorance as to it. Here, by 'ignorance,' I mean *ignorance;* accordingly no advice can be given as to how to expect it, or to treat it, in 'practice' or any other way." Similarly, aspects of the transaction which cannot be reached from any other point can be known only by the particular participant and are unique to him.

Each one of us is, therefore, constantly playing a dual role. First, we are experiencing our own unique participation with all its intellectual and valueful overtones, many of which cannot even be verbalized without being lost. Secondly, we are constantly trying to abstract from this total experience those aspects which are or can be experienced at the same time by other participants. It is here that we are constantly in danger of falling into what Whitehead has called the "fallacy of misplaced concreteness" if we assign greater concreteness, that is, a higher degree of external reality, to the abstracted aspects than to the total experience from which they are abstracted.

Perceptions are unique to the perceiver, but common sense and experience tell us that there are areas of communality. Indeed, if everyone perceived entirely differently from everyone else, it is difficult to imagine how any agreement or social activity could be possible. No two people can have identical personal behavioral centers if for no other reason than that they cannot occupy the same space at the same time. But their positions can overlap to a greater or lesser extent, and to the extent that they do, including not only orientation in time and space but also interests and purposes, the two persons will tend to have common perceptions and common experiences.

PERCEPTION AS EXTERNALIZATION

Probably the most obvious aspect of the experience of perception is that it is externally oriented, that is, the things we see, and hear, and taste, and touch are experienced as existing outside of ourselves and as possessing for themselves the characteristics which we perceive in them. But it is also clear that perception is part of the experience of the individual. One essential feature of perception, then, is the external orientation of certain aspects of experience. In perceiving, parts of our own experience are attributed to events external to ourselves in whose independent existence we firmly believe. As Schilder has expressed it, "The act of perceiving in itself so implies the act of considering it real that the latter can be called an attribute of the act of perceiving." When we perceive, we externalize certain aspects of our experience and thereby create for ourselves our own world of things and people, of sights and sounds, of tastes and touches. Without taking any metaphysical position regarding the existence of a real world independent of experience, we can nevertheless assert that the world-as-experienced has no meaning and cannot be defined independent of the experience. *The world as we experience it* is the product of perception, not the cause of it.

Certain aspects of experience are definitely and surely attributed to the external world. Bridgman has pointed out, "Perception we have always had with us and we take it completely for granted. We *see things* out there in space moving about, and that is all there is to it. We accept these perceptions at their face value and, on them as a foundation, we build the pattern of our 'reality.' To this reality, we ascribe an absolute existence transcending its origin." Clearly, not all experience is externalized, however. Other aspects are just as definitely considered to be personal, subjective and having no external reference. Still other aspects lie in a never-never land in between. It is important, therefore, to ask such questions as: What aspects of experience are viewed as representing something independent of the experience, and what aspects are not? Why, indeed, does anyone ever come to believe in the independent existence of an external world? And what are the factors that determine which aspect of experience is selected as representing this external reality? The answers to these questions lie beyond the scope of this book, but the problems raised by the questions lurk behind any study in the field of perception.

It should be noted that it is not immediately and simply evident what kinds of experiences can profitably be externalized. Some people on some occasions may externalize experiences which might more effectively be considered as subjective or vice versa. In psychiatry, one important part of therapy may well be that the patient learns to externalize some aspects of experience which he has heretofore not externalized, and, probably more important, that he learns not to externalize many experiences which in the past he did —that he recognizes as his own experience certain things which he used to attribute to external events.

The view that in perceiving the individual creates his own psychological environment by attributing aspects of his experience to an external environment is historically quite recent. The early study of perception was concerned with the question of what is done *by* the environment *to* the organism while perceiving. This view that something goes "into" the organism has persisted from the time of the Greeks right up to much present-day psychology with its interest in "stimulus determination" of perception. Psychologists studying perception found early that certain variations in objective or physiological factors produced marked subjective variations. This naturally led to the idea of correspondence between subjective factors on the one hand and objective and physiological factors on the other. Since an alteration of objective and physiological factors could so easily be shown to cause subjective effects, and since the converse could not so easily be demonstrated, the assumption was built up that the subjective aspects of perception had their origin largely in the corresponding objective factors and the accompanying physiological disturbances they caused.

Whereas the early studies started with the object and went to the organism, the direction has now been reversed; we start with the organism and work toward the object. This simple change has produced a revolution in thinking with implications which will be pointed out throughout the rest of this book. The question of perception has been rephrased so that today we are concerned with what is done *by* the organism. What does the organism actually do when it perceives? To say that the organism externalizes certain aspects of its experience does not answer the question but

Dr. Mark Plotkin

Conservation International

1015 18th ST N.W.

Suite 1000

Washington, D.C. 20036

202-429-5660

merely points out one characteristic of the process—that the study of perception takes the active, perceiving individual as its point of departure.

The three major characteristics of perception can be summarized by saying that *perceiving is that part of the process of living by which each one of us from his own particular point of view creates for himself the world in which he has his life's experiences and through which he strives to gain his satisfactions.* Before we proceed with formulating the problem of perception, it is important to point out that each characteristic of the perceptual process carries with it its own difficulties and obstacles in the way of understanding.

SOME DIFFICULTIES IN THE STUDY OF PERCEPTION

We have already shown that perceiving is an integral part of every transaction of living, that indeed it is difficult for any of us to think of ourselves as living without perceiving. To perceive is as natural and necessary as to sleep, yet its very naturalness and all-pervasiveness make perception a difficult subject matter to grasp. Most of us would probably be willing to say, "I perceive the way I do because that's the way I am. Things look the way they do because that's the way they are." But while this statement may have a superficial validity, it blinds us to important questions as to the function and development of the perceptual process. Many of the findings of the scientific study of perception go quite contrary to this common sense view and their acceptance is made difficult by the very naturalness of perceiving, accentuated by the fallacy of misplaced concreteness referred to earlier.

The fact of externalization presents an even more serious barrier to the study of perception. We tend to believe that things as we see them exist "out there" apart from us and independent of the experience of seeing. This belief is strong in all of us and, as we shall see later, it must be strong if we are to be able to act at all effectively. But the danger of this belief when studying perception lies in the fact that it provides us in a sense with the answer to our problem in advance of our study. If the objects of perception exist in their own right as perceived, then all we have to do is fit the perception to an already existing object. The error of this view was nicely expressed by Whitehead when he said,

"We must not slip into the fallacy of assuming that we are comparing a given world with given perceptions of it. The physical world is in some general sense of the term a deduced concept. Our problem is, in fact, to fit the world to our perceptions and not our perceptions to the world." While Whitehead. was referring to the physical sciences, what he says applies even more forcibly to our consideration of the world as perceived.

Another serious difficulty in the study of perception is the fact that perceiving is a personal experience, that it can be accounted for adequately only from the point of view of the perceiving individual's personal behavioral center. This necessitates an approach to the study of perception which differs in important ways from that used in most scientific studies. When one scientist reports his work to another, he makes statements which, while they refer to natural phenomena, are actually reducible to statements about what the other scientist will experience if he does certain things.

This is essentially the operational view which has in recent years gained widespread acceptance. The impetus for operationism came from Bridgman in physics, with the recognition that concepts such as distance have different meanings in different contexts. The concept is, therefore, a construct of the observer and not "a thing in itself." It follows that if the variables with which an experimenter deals are products of the experimenter's ingenuity and cannot be specified by pointing to them, then they must be specified by pointing to the procedures employed by the experimenter in creating his constructs. It is only by pointing out the procedures employed in experimentation that the investigator can convey to others the constructs he is dealing with.

Operational statements of this sort are an important part of the science of psychology. They are essentially statements in which one psychologist tells another what he will experience if he performs certain operations. They say nothing about the experience of the subject on whom these operations are performed. Such statements are indispensable to psychology but they are not enough. You as a person are not usually interested in how well two other people who happen to call themselves psychologists can predict to each other what behavior of yours they will observe under certain circumstances. You are interested ordinarily in your own personal experiences. Psychology, therefore, in addition to operational statements made from the standpoint of an outside observer, also employs statements made from the standpoint of the individual's personal behavioral center, or, in other terms, psychology makes use of first person statements as well as third person statements. Without first person statements we have a psychology of zombies or, to use a popular engineering term, of "black boxes."

But there is an even more important reason why the study of perception in particular has to be undertaken from the point of view of the perceiver. The scientist himself is also and always a perceiver. When he makes operational statements he is abstracting from his own personal experience certain aspects which he believes are or can be shared by another person. Any scientist who can make statements about perception as if he were not himself a perceiver is doing more than committing a logical fallacy; he is going contrary to the findings of science itself. As Bridgman has well summarized it, "The observer must somehow be included in the system. The point of view of classical physics, and I believe also of all orthodox human thinking up to the present, was that the observer is a passive spectator, expressed sometimes by saying that what he observes would be the same whether he were watching or not. Quantum theory points out that this is only an approximation valid in the realm of large objects. The very act of observing a small object involves a reaction between the object and the observer, a reaction that must be allowed for in reconstructing the system from observation. To which we now add the insight that the relationship between the observed and the observer is a much more intimate relationship than these quantum considerations would suggest, and that it is in fact meaningless to try to separate observer and observed, or to speak of an object independent of an observer, or, for that matter, of an observer in the absence of objects of observation."

THE CENTRAL PROBLEM OF PERCEPTION

Perhaps because of these difficulties an understanding of perception is one of the most fascinating and central problems a psychologist faces. Our perceptions give each of us the only world we know. It is the world in which we act, and we act in terms of our perceptions. Our perceptions provide us with predictions as to what will probably happen if we act in a particular way. Our actions will be effective only insofar as the predictions derived from our perceptions correspond to what we actually experience when we act. This, then, is the central problem of perception—to study the degree of *correspondence* between the significances which we *externalize* and those which we *encounter* and to understand the process by which this correspondence is achieved.

Before proceeding, we will discuss in more detail what is meant by stating the problem this way. For this is the crucial step in our inquiry. It is the way in which an investigator poses his problem that determines where he will come out; that determines what aspects of the phenomena which he is studying he will feel have a bearing on the problem; that determines which of these he will use as the basis for variables in empirical investigation and what methodological procedures he will follow or try to devise. Further, the formulation of the problem for investigation must contain within itself the possibility of going beyond what is already scientifically established if it is to satisfy the definition of scientific research. If the formulation of the problem does not do this, then the succeeding steps in investigation are futile. We can resolve some of the difficulties in the understanding of perception only insofar as we have problemized those difficulties adequately.

With this in mind, let us examine more carefully the three key concepts in our problem as we stated them. "Correspondence" will be used in the sense of correspondence between two kinds of experience and never in the sense of identity between experience and "reality." Of course, for purposes of experimentation it is frequently necessary to deduce the second kind of experience—that is, what the observer would experience if he acted—from some other kind of knowledge gained through outside observation. When this is done, the implication is always present that it is a substitute for potential experiences on the part of the perceiver. The term "externalize" we have already discussed. It refers to those aspects of the experience of the perceiver to which he attributes a reality independent of the experience. The validity of this attribution can only be checked through some future behavior—when he encounters aspects of the transaction independent of himself. "Encounter," then, implies the full range of experience. It involves perception plus all other aspects of human experience, including the most advanced intellectual, aesthetic and valueful experiences. Perceptual correspondence implies that the sum total of experience gained while dealing with the external world is similar or identical to that which was expected.

While it is implicit in all we have said so far, it should be emphasized that the study of perceptual correspondence from this point of view also requires a consideration of the *purposes* of the perceiver. For the significances we encounter in the course of acting can only be evaluated in terms of what we intend to do. Any statement about perceptual correspondence necessarily implies a statement about purposes. Thus, it becomes clear why accurate perceptions of the behavior of other people are so difficult to achieve. For other people, like ourselves, have their own purposes and it is by no means a simple matter to acquire a correspondence between the purposes we attribute to other people and the purposes they may actually be pursuing.

The Perceptual Process

We have said that perceiving is that part of the process of living by which each one of us, from his own particular point of view, creates for himself the world within which he has his life's experiences and through which he strives to gain his satisfactions. This view of perception (seen as a sub-process of the more general process of living) is in accord with recent thinking about the very nature of the process of living itself. After thoroughly examining contemporary views, Cantril has proposed that living be defined "as a process in which an organism participates in the creation of an environment through which it can carry out its purposes." Such a definition "gives us a general specification applicable to the bird building its nest, the salmon returning to the river, as well as the human being, whether child or adult, participating in the multifarious transaction of living."

The malleability of the environment in the face of determined onslaught by groups of organisms is more and more being recognized by the students of biology and evolution. The old view of a fixed environment to which organisms must adapt or perish is being rapidly superseded by a view which emphasizes the organism's creative role in shaping his own environment. "The organisms can create their own environment," says Whitehead. "For this purpose, the single organism is almost helpless. The adequate forces require societies of cooperating organisms. But with such cooperation, and in proportion to the effort put forward, the environment has a plasticity which alters the whole ethical aspect of evolution."

Of all organisms certainly man has achieved the greatest degree of control over his environment. His technical ability to create a physical environment ever more suited to his needs is clear. Not so obvious, but perhaps even more important, is man's amazing ability and flexibility in creating a psychological environment for himself. Man in his social aspect creates for himself a common physical environment through which all men act; each man in his individual aspect creates for himself the psychological world within which he has his life's experiences.

We can here do no more than point out that these two aspects do not operate separately and independently; rather they are interrelated and can perhaps best be considered as different ways of looking at the same thing. The kind of psychological world a person creates for himself depends in part, as we shall see, on the kind of world he encounters as he acts. Similarly, the kind of environment he will strive to create, that is, the kind of environment which he feels will most likely provide his desired satisfactions, will depend very largely on the kind of psychological world he has created for himself which, in the last analysis, is the only world he knows. When we recognize that the environment man is today creating includes his own social and cultural systems as well as tools sufficient for destroying them and man himself along with them, we get some appreciation of the immense importance of understanding that part of the process which is each man's creation of his own unique world of experience.

EXPERIENCED SIGNIFICANCE

For the purpose of simplifying discussion, experience can be classified into a few major categories. This does not imply that these categories represent distinct "entities" with sharp breaks or dividing lines between them. The classification that seems most useful is in terms of the different types of significances which a person senses in his own experience. There are four broad classes of experienced significances which enter into the perceptual process and which will be outlined here in a manner sufficiently general to apply to all perceiving. The specific relation of these otherwise abstract statements to the problems of visual space perception will be made clearer later.

There is, however, one additional type of perceptual significance peculiar to man to which we will not explicitly refer in this discussion: man's unique capacity to receive abstract messages in complex coding through his senses. We refer here not only to language in its written or spoken form, but also to such diverse communication devices as mathematical symbols, Indian sign language, and African drum messages, as well as, to a certain extent, all aesthetic productions. In man the receiving of symbolic messages is undoubtedly one of the most important functions of perception. In lower animals it can be observed, if at all, only in a most primitive and stereotyped way. Seeing and hearing are the most important perceptual channels for the reception of coded messages; for example, reading a written word or listening to a spoken word. But touch can be formally coded, as in Braille, and informally coded, as in the lover's touch conveying a thousand meanings. Theoretically any sense modality can be coded and used in this way, although in practice man has used only these three: vision, hearing, and touch. In studying human perception, we have constantly to bear in mind that it is impossible to have any perception which is devoid of symbolic content. Furthermore, this symbolic content is not some excess baggage added to the perception but is an integral and inseparable part of it.

It is essential to recognize throughout the study of perception that man's ability to communicate with each other through symbolic coded messages is not some special faculty added to perception but rather is itself a product of the special features of the perceptual process unique to man. The major differences between the perception of symbolic messages and other perception lies in the fact that in the former the coding is a product of social consensus while in the latter each individual develops his own personal code. However, since an adequate discussion of this would carry us into the field of linguistics, symbolism and meaning, from this point on we will deal with perception without specific reference to symbolic content. With this proviso in mind, we can discuss the important classes of significances which enter into the study of perception.

"Thing" significances. This term refers to the world of objects and people insofar as we experience them as entities apart from ourselves possessing their own characteristics and spatial-temporal locations. For example, if we look at a piece of paper or a desk, we attribute to each certain characteristic sizes, shapes, and material properties. We experience things as wholes, so that if we see the head of a cow which is joined by the edge of a barn we assume

that the rest of the cow exists although cut off from our view by the barn. We learn to think of buildings or automobiles as having certain sizes and we are struck by "tall" buildings in Europe or by "small" automobiles in the U.S. We come to think of certain ethnic or cultural groups as possessing their own particular characteristics, and as we become what we call "prejudiced" we perceive these characteristics as fixed properties of more and more people according to the particular purpose such a grouping serves for us.

Sequential significances.   The world of objects does not exist passively and statically for our observation. Very rarely if ever do we contemplate a completely unchanging world where all sights, all sounds, all touches, tastes, and smells are static, frozen and fixed. Rather, events of one kind or another are constantly occurring around us, new events following the previous in a never-ending series of sequences. Night follows day; the stone we let go of drops to the ground; a rubber ball bounces. In order to increase the reliability of sequential significances, man has created a bewildering variety of artifacts. These tools and man-made devices are generally designed for the purpose of ensuring that certain sequential events will follow each other in predictable directions. Thus a baseball used in league games has to meet certain standards; automobiles in many states have to be inspected to see that brakes operate properly when the pedal is pushed. And the history of every culture shows how men and women throughout the ages have devised norms, rituals, rules and laws to increase the number and reliability of common sequential significances which enable people to live together more effectively and satisfyingly. For example, the marriage ceremony, which exists in some form in nearly all cultures, symbolizes the introduction of a new social relationship into the long chain of past and future sequential occurrences that constitute living. A list of all the sequences constantly going on about us would be endless. Out of this tremendous multiplicity of sequences we take account of, or "register," only a comparatively few; namely, those which are both relevant to our purposes and have some degree of repeatability. We attribute no significance to any happening which is completely out of relationship to our purposes or our experiences.

Action significances.   Although occasionally we all passively observe sequential events from the outside, more frequently we enter into the sequence at some point as active participants. The events which follow as sequences to our own actions have special significance in the perceptual process. When we act, we act for a purpose; we intend to accomplish some desired result. Whether or not we do achieve our intentions provides us with a measure of the adequacy of the psychological world in which we live. Thus the child gradually builds up a number of assumptions as to what effect will follow some action he initiates, such as the rebound of a rubber ball thrown on the floor. The farmer, carpenter, or surgeon learns through repeated testing of his actions how to participate effectively in a chain of sequential events in order to experience the desired consequences of his behavior. The saying that practice makes perfect symbolizes the importance of experiences in which we actively participate.

Evaluative significances. As a rule, in any concrete situation into which we enter as active participants, each of us is constantly faced with alternative courses of action. Evaluation among these alternatives is made on the basis of the relative probability that each possible course of action will lead to the desired sequences, will produce the desired results. In general, this is a tremendously complex process, since an almost infinite number of sub-probabilities relating to each of the other classes of significances must be taken into account.

There are two main categories of this kind of evaluation which can be separated for descriptive purposes, although in concrete experience they are interwoven and almost never encountered independently. (1) *What-for* evaluations involve selection among alternative goals on the basis of which goal offers the greater probability of providing us with the value satisfactions we seek out of life. This kind of *value judgment,* which will not be expanded in any detail in this book, enters at least implicitly into every perception. For example, a college student with athletic ability may wonder whether he should try out for the football team or have more time for his class work or for general social life. For him, there is no question of how to do either one. The choice is a choice of alternate goals to pursue, and will affect in many ways how he perceives the world about him. (2) *How-to-do* evaluations enter more explicitly into the perceptual process. They involve selection among alternative courses of action once the immediate goal has been decided upon. Suppose our student decides to go out for football, makes the team, and becomes a quarterback confronted with a situation where, ball in hand, he can pass to one of several receivers or keep the ball and run. His choice here is one of how-to-do. The goal—to win the game—is not the problem for decision. But how he perceives the other players on the field and what he decides to do are interrelated and mutually affect each other.

This brief list does not exhaust the significances which combine to make up any total real-life experience. They are, however, those which appear most relevant to the study of perception. They go far beyond the dictionary definition of perception, which is subsumed under the first category.

Although we divided the experienced significances which enter into the perceptual process into four discrete groups, it is impossible to draw any sharp line between the various aspects of experience. "Thing" merges imperceptibly into "thing-in-motion" which is already a primitive sequence. Sequential events involving "things" other than the participant merge gradually into sequences into which the participant enters as another "thing." But these are almost indistinguishable from self-initiated but non-purposive sequences which in turn are quickly replaced by full-blown intentional or purposive action. Purposive action almost at once involves evaluation between alternative how-to-do's and quickly leads to what-for evaluations of the highest order. All of these significances from the lowliest "thing" to the highest "value" are completely and simultaneously involved in any concrete perceptual experience.

It is probably true that any significance which is experienced can be externalized; even our highest order value satisfactions can be put "out there" and have attributed to them an existence independent of the fact of experiencing them. For example, some theories of aesthetics put our own aesthetic experience "into" the painting or the music. But such a view fails to recognize that the beauty of a picture is part of the experience of the viewer as he participates in a particular transaction into which the painting also enters as an integral aspect but *not* as the carrier of a "beauty" which "exists" in the painting prior to and independent of any concrete transaction. Similarly, the romantic lover puts his own value experiences "into" the person of the loved one and sees them as "entities" comprising part of that person, independent of any concrete transactions between the two.

As we have pointed out, learning which aspects of experience to externalize and which not to is not a simple or obvious task. Probably everyone will agree that perception involves the externalization of at least two classes of events; independent existence is attributed to (1) things or objects in their spatial or temporal relationships and (2) causes or causal relationships between things or objects.

Actual experience, however, consists of a constant flow of sequential events; that is, one pattern of events follows as a sequence of another pattern of events, as one transaction flows into the next. From these sequences we abstract from our experience in two ways. First, we abstract certain potential sequential significances at a particular time and place; these we then label objects. Secondly, we abstract a particular selection of specific sequences in a particular spatial and temporal relationship; these we label causes or causal relationships. The function of this kind of abstraction is to make it possible to deal with a limited number of sequences and therefore to act effectively. It is impossible to deal simultaneously with all the sequences constantly occurring in our ongoing experience. This, then, is the genesis of externalized thing and sequential significances.

BUILT IN OR BUILT UP?

When we ask ourselves deceptively simple questions about where these significances come from, how any person acquires the particular significances which combine to make up his own perceptual experience, we find ourselves plunged into the midst of one of the most bitter and persistent controversies in the history of philosophy as well as of psychology. For the question has traditionally been posed by asking to what extent perceptions are learned and to what extent they are inborn. Fortunately, in relation to perception, this controversy has tended to drop out of sight in recent years not because the question has been answered but because it has come to be considered meaningless.

The reason for this change in viewpoint is clear. Perceptions, as we have seen, never appear abstractly as entities in themselves which can be examined and studied. Rather, perception can only be observed as one aspect of a concrete experience. More correctly, the significances *are* experience; it becomes meaningless to ask whether particular significances are learned or inborn. Meaningfully, we can ask only under what concrete conditions does a particular significance enter into the perceptual process of a particular observer. Even if we were to find that some significances are invariably reported under *all* conditions or by *all* people, we may still properly hesitate to draw the conclusion that we are dealing with an inherent property of the organism. The concrete experimental problem is that of studying the relative continuity and constancy of various significances under different conditions and for different people. What kinds of significances change most readily through the process of experiencing them, and conversely, what kinds of experiences are accompanied by the greatest change in significances?

THE FORMATION OF ASSUMPTIONS

Any present perceptual experience consists of a total complex of significances. All previous experiences have been similarly composed. Through the course of experiencing, certain significances are found by the perceiver to have high probabilities of being related to each other and to other aspects of the situation. Other relationships have a low probability of occurring. These probabilities, high or low, are in turn weighted in terms of the relevance of the unique situation in which they have occurred to the larger purposes and values of the experiencing person. All this is accomplished through a largely unconscious process and results in a set of assumptions or weighted averages of previous experiences which are brought to the present occasion, and play a principal role in determining how the occasion is experienced. For each of us the sum total of these assumptions can be said to constitute our *assumptive world*. The assumptive world of any particular individual at any particular time determines his perceptions, that is, provides him with predictions of probable significances. His assumptive world is, therefore, in a very real sense the only world which he knows.

Each of us builds his assumptive world largely in an unconscious and non-intellectual way in the process of adjustment and development as he goes about the business of life, that is, as he tries to act effectively to achieve his purposes. We often use many of our assumptions without being at all aware of them, such as those involved in habits, stereotypes, and a host of perceptual activities. We become aware of other assumptions from time to time as they become relevant to the situation at hand, such as loyalties, expectancies, ideals. Still others such as intellectual abstractions can be brought to voluntary recall. Our actions cannot be effective unless and until each one of us builds up an assumptive world that has some degree of constancy and verifiability.

THE WEIGHING PROCESS

Perhaps the most significant point to be made concerning assumptions as they concretely enter into the transaction is that they are rarely, if ever, in complete harmony. On the contrary, any concrete experience involves the achievement of some sort of resolution of many assumptions that are more or less incompatible and sometimes directly contradictory. This resolution is accomplished by means of an unconscious "weighing process"; this is a figurative description of an as yet imperfectly understood function. The particular weight given to each assumption in this unconscious calculation is a product of at least three factors. First, each assumption is undoubtedly weighted on a probability basis. That is, assumptions which have frequently and consistently proved valid in the past will tend to be weighted most heavily. This point has been made, in other terminology, by Brunswik, in whose "probabilistic functionalism" weightings are determined on the basis of "ecological validity." Brunswik is in error, however, when he assumes that weights are based solely on a probability basis. A second criterion for the weight given an assumption lies in the overall significance to the individual of each particular experience into which the assumption entered and its importance within that experience. This consideration makes possible extreme cases of traumatic weighting, but also undoubtedly figures less dramatically in every experience. Finally, an assumption will be weighted in the immediate situation depending upon its relevancy to the specific purposes of the moment. Each assumption, then, enters into the weighing process with a weight determined on a probability basis adjusted in terms of its previous importance to the individual and its relationship to the immediate transaction.

It follows from these considerations that perceptions can change through two different processes. One process takes place within the already existing framework of assumptions and consists of altering the weight without changing the assumptions themselves. The effects of this *perceptual re-weighting* process become evident only when conflicts are present. In a conflict situation, however, the particular resolution achieved, and hence the resultant experience, will be changed in accord with the newly assigned weights. The second process of perceptual change calls for the acquiring of totally new assumptions. This *perceptual re-learning* process is more fundamental and can change the entire perceptual experience of the individual.

BEING AWARE OF VERSUS TAKING ACCOUNT OF

It is evident from the preceding discussion that neither assumptions nor any other aspects of the perceptual process necessarily enter, as such, directly into the awareness of the perceiver. However, as Whitehead has pointed out, "We certainly do take account of things of which at the time we have no explicit cognition. We can even have a cognitive memory of the taking account, without having had a contemporaneous cognition." It is useful in perceptual studies to bear in mind this distinction between what we are aware of as differentiated from what we take account of.

The range of awareness may vary widely from one perceptual situation to another. The perceiver may on occasion have his awareness restricted to a single object or possibly a single attribute of the object, although such extreme restriction is probably quite rare outside the psychophysical laboratory. On the other hand, awareness may extend to a multitude of objects in their spatial and temporal relations, their causal interconnections, their significance for our own actions as well as all their implications for the furthering of our purposes and the achievement of our value satisfactions and aesthetic pleasures. But regardless of how restricted or how wideranging a perceiver's awareness may be, what he is aware of comes about through a process in which he takes account of many more and different aspects than he is ever aware of.

THE DEFINITION OF PERCEPTION

It may be well to summarize what we have learned so far about perception in a general statement which may be taken as a definition of perception. We have seen that perceiving refers to the process by which a particular person, from his particular behavioral center, attributes significances to his immediate environmental situation. It is this attribution of significance which transforms a neutral environmental "happening" into a meaningful event. The significances which the person attributes are those which he has discovered from past experiences have furthered his purposes. If the analysis of the significances of the immediate environmental situation provides a correct prediction as to the significances of the environmental situation, we say that there is correspondence between perceptual awareness and the environmental situation. To the degree that this analysis provides incorrect predictions as to the significance of the environmental situation, there is a lack of correspondence between perceptual awareness and the environmental situation. Both of these conditions play important roles in perception as it enters into the concrete process of living.

THE TIME-ORIENTATION OF PERCEPTION

We have discussed perception so far primarily as a present experience with its roots in the past. This time-orientation is in accord with naive observation and with the traditional approach of psychology. Perception certainly seems to be of the world as it is right now, or perhaps, as it was a moment ago. Indeed the definition of perception frequently appears in psychology texts as "The awareness of immediately present objects." But naive observation and tradition are both inadequate. While present and past are involved in the perceptual process, the chief time-orientation in perceiving is toward the future. The primary function of perception is neither revelation of the present nor remembrance of the past; it is prediction of the future.

If we were to close the theoretical discussion of perception without making this time-orientation explicit, the problem would still be distorted in such a way that it could not be solved. For just as past perceptions were once present perceptions, so every present perception is in a sense the anticipated future of a past experience. The process by which the present becomes the past of the future is basic to perception. As Laotze said, "What is is the was of what shall be."

EXPERIENCING THE CONSEQUENCES OF OUR OWN ACTIONS

The orientation toward the future is a product of the characteristic of perceptions which we have called *externalization*. Perceiving, as we have seen, provides us with predictions of the significances we will probably encounter in the external world. But we can come to grips with externality only by doing something, by acting. We discover the significances of the external situation only by experiencing the consequences of our own actions.

The experienced consequences of every action provide a check on the perceptual prediction on which the action was based. In this sense the perceptual process operating in all of us is quite analogous to the process of scientific inquiry. Every action can be thought of as an experimental test of an hypothesis which is appropriately modified or confirmed as the result of our test through action. One psychological result of any action, then, is a change in the probabilities unconsciously assigned to the particular assumptions on which that action was based. The probability is changed in proportion to the weight given to that particular experience, resulting in new assumptions, new predictions, new externalized significances.

It is important that we differentiate two ways in which assumptions, and consequently perceptions, change through experiencing the effects of our actions. First, every action we undertake is a check on an assumption. Hence every action affects the subjective probability assigned to that assumption. Second, and of much greater importance, there are actions that bring about changes in the assumptions themselves or lead to formation of new assumptions. These are actions whose experienced consequences are either contradictory to an assumption or not related to any existing assumption—"unsuccessful" actions, hitches, resulting in surprise, disappointment, frustration, or the awareness of a new problem to be resolved.

HITCHES

Successful actions can only confirm what we know. Hitches provide the occasions for increasing the scope and adequacy of our assumptions. An understanding of the nature of hitches as related to the perceptual process therefore becomes of paramount importance.

A hitch arises if we do not experience a significance which we expected to experience. Hitches can be encountered in any of the four major kinds of experienced significances discussed earlier. We can see the world of things around us with their own particular characteristics and positions in space, and then discover that in one or more ways we were incorrect in this perception. The objects may not possess the characteristics we perceived in them or they may not be where we thought they were. We may experience people as having certain emotions, values, purposes, or other characteristics which we later find out they do not have. Or we can expect certain events to follow as sequences of other events and discover that they do not follow. Anyone who has offered his hand for a handshake which has been rejected knows that the incorrect prediction of even such a simple sequence of events provides a hitch of some magnitude.

But since hitches are revealed only through action and since action is always undertaken with some goal in mind, hitches ultimately can be reduced to the kind of evaluative experience described as the fourth type of experienced significance. Every hitch is either the result of a failure to achieve a particular goal, that is, of inadequate "how-to-do" predictions, or else the result of a failure to experience a hoped-for satisfaction resulting from an incorrect "what-for" prediction. On whatever level the actual lack of correspondence between externalized and encountered significances may occur, whether on the level of things, on the level of sequences, or on the level of our own actions, hitches are always experienced in terms of the frustration of our purposes.

THE NOVELTY OF THE IMMEDIATE SITUATION

Completely successful action—action without any trace of an experienced hitch—is more of a myth than a reality. Completely successful action could occur only if the world were completely determined, and if the acting individual possessed all the necessary information to make a perfect prediction. We need not argue the question of determinism or indeterminism in the "real" world, but can simply point out that the world of experience is, to a greater or lesser extent, always indeterminate. Every immediate concrete situation we face has a certain degree of novelty. To this extent it is unpredictable, indeterminate; it has some degree of novelty which we cannot completely predict from our previous experience. Some lack of correspondence is, therefore, a necessary part of perception in every concrete transaction of living.

As pointed out, lack of correspondence can occur as a function of the physical, physiological, or psychological aspects involved in experience or in any combination of these. We can see now that there is invariably in the immediate situation some aspect which has never been encountered in the past. Change is the rule of nature. John Dewey once said that what we call *permanence* is an aspect of some situation that is merely changing so slowly that we cannot recognize it, such, for example, as the slow erosion of the Rocky Mountains. But more generally in life, both things and people do change from hour to hour, day to day, or year to year. Social situations do not repeat themselves exactly. Even when situations have remained so similar from one occasion to another that effective behavior becomes habitual, we become aware of change when we operate on the basis of habit at the wrong time or the wrong place; for example, when we trip over a curbing which we failed to notice was higher than those we had adjusted to.

Every concrete situation potentially involves an element of choice as a product of its degree of novelty. Thus every participant in a concrete occasion of living is faced with a choice among uncertainties. These choices, or evaluations, are part of living. "How-to-do's" that are relatively certain may sometimes be expected to be accompanied by relatively meager satisfactions. "What-for" goals with a high probability of producing great value satisfaction can perhaps be accomplished only through extremely uncertain "how-to-do's." And these evaluations must be made in the face of the further uncertainty that the novelty of the situation we face is never revealed to us before we act. Even the degree of uncertainty itself is uncertain.

ACTION AND CERTAINTY

How can anyone act in the face of the probability of failure? Action implies certainty. If the perceptions on which actions are based necessarily prove to be to some extent imperfect, and if our actions will inevitably be unsuccessful to this extent, we might eventually reach a condition where we would hesitate to act at all. The answer to the question is to be found in the nature of the perceptual process—when the predictive reliability of a perception becomes high enough we act "as if" we were dealing with certainty. Even if the predictive reliability is low, so that we lack a sense of surety, when we finally do act we must act with certainty if we are to have any chance of being successful. One aspect of perceiving, then, is the creation of certainty out of uncertainty or probability. Every perception is an act of creation; every action is an act of faith. Every action is based on the belief that highly probable events are certain events. It is an act of faith in the reliability of one's own assumptions, of faith in oneself. Accordingly one product of perceiving is our creation of a world of *functional* absolutes. At any given moment, these functional absolutes are treated as if they were certain but, concurrently, are held open for modification.

FORM AND FLOW

Two apparently opposing forces struggle with each other throughout the process of perceiving. In order to live we must act. In order to act we must have some feeling of certainty, some *form* to serve as a springboard from which to jump into the future. But by the very nature of things we are constantly faced with novelty, with *flow*, and are thus constantly forced to modify our assumptions. Every perception is based upon a form which we take to be permanent and unchanging. But every perception and every action also alters this form to a greater or lesser extent. Every time we act on the basis of a perception we in some way confirm or deny, modify or alter the assumptions we began with, the assumptions that contributed to the perception we used as a directive for our actions.

If our actions are successful and satisfying in terms of our purposes, our world of predictability, of security, of form is reinforced and provides us with the sense of surety essential for acting again. Actions which prove to be unsuccessful or unsatisfying in terms of our purposes disclose opportunities for revising our predictions, for change of form, for flow in keeping with the flow of conditions. If we meet these opportunities with modifications which lead to greater success and greater satisfactions, we experience the feeling of growth, of development, of creativity. Predictions modified and revised provide growth through failure. Probabilities increased through more adequate predictions provide greater surety for action.

The human being, as all living organisms, ceaselessly attempts to create an environment within which to carry out his purposes. In every situation of living, perception-in-operation is a process of prediction in the face of uncertainty for action on the basis of faith.

Part Two

THE VISUAL
SPACE CUES

IV

Visual Cues, Equivalent Configurations and The Invariance Hypothesis

The study of visual space perception has traditionally been oriented around the concept of "cue," which will be used as the unifying concept in this book, too. The term will be examined in some detail so that when we use it there will be no uncertainty as to its meaning. In this chapter, after discussing the concept of visual cues in a general way, we will treat one special aspect, the relevant relationships between the external object and the impinging light energy, summed up in the concept of *equivalent configurations*. Following this, the question of the relationship, if any, between equivalent configurations and perceptions will be treated. This will lead us into a consideration of the *invariance hypothesis*. In the remaining four chapters of this section the various space cues will be dealt with separately.

The traditional concept of "cue" has persisted in psychology over the years in spite of attempts to replace it. It is still with us because it has a basic validity which is to be found in its implicit recognition of the symbolic nature of the perceptual process as it functions in any concrete transaction. It seems unnecessary and, in fact, undesirable to approach the study of space perception by any other road. This is not to say that "cue" is not in need of definition and constant reevaluation in the light of the latest scientific evidence.

PRELIMINARY DESCRIPTION OF THE VISUAL CUES

We will start the discussion of cues with a list of those which have been enumerated and studied up to the present time. This listing is for the purpose of provisionally identifying the cues, each of which will be specified more rigorously in subsequent chapters.

The list of cues is quoted from Graham and was selected as being representative of current definitions.

1. *Size.* "Our discrimination of distances is dependent on the size of the retinal image provided by an object."

2. *Overlay, interposition or superposition.* "The cue of interposition occurs when an overlapping object is said to be nearer than an overlapped object."

3. *Linear perspective.* "A constant distance between points subtends a smaller and smaller angle at the eye as the points recede from the subject."

4. *Aerial perspective.* "When surface details of an object do not provide conditions for requisite visual contrasts, a subject reports that the object seems far off."

5. *Movement parallax.* "When a subject's eyes move with respect to the environment, or when the environment moves with respect to a subject's eyes, a differential angular velocity exists between the line of sight to a fixated object and the line of sight to any other object in the visual field."

6. *Light and shade.* "Various combinations of shadow and highlight are reported as objects having various dimensions and lying at different distances."

7. *Accommodation.* "Differential aspects of 'blur circles' in a retinal image may elicit spatial discrimination." (To this may also be added the older notion of a kinaesthetic cue.)

8. *Convergence.* "When an object is at a great distance, lines of fixation to the object are parallel. When the object is near at hand, the subject's eyes are turned in a coordinated manner so that the lines of fixation converge on the object. Convergence may serve as a cue for depth responses."

9. *Stereoscopic vision.* "When a subject regards an object in space, the retinal image in the left eye is different from the retinal image in the right eye. The difference in retinal images serves as the basis for many spatial discriminations."

To this list we have to add at least the following: *shape, color, brightness,* and *position in the field.*

While the relationship of these cues to space perception seems intuitively obvious to most people, their separate identification and intellectualization covers the entire span of human thought. Two main historical epochs of discovery of the visual cues can be identified, and behind each lies a different motivation.

The impetus for the first epoch came from an interest in pictorial art, which seems to date far into the prehistoric periods of man's development. The earliest visual cues to be discovered were those of use to the artist: size, shape and perspective, overlay, color, brightness, light and shadow, aerial perspective, and position in the field. All of these cues were used by artists long before they were intellectualized either by the artists themselves or by others. Almost without exception, examples of their use can be found in prehistoric or ancient art, although it was not until Leonardo that most of them were separately and consciously conceptualized. Even Leonardo neglected some, it is generally supposed, because they are too obvious to mention. Artistic experimentation involving the space cues (in contrast to their discovery) is never-ending, while the scientific study of some of them is still in a primitive stage. The first major epoch of discovery of the visual space cues, then, was motivated by the needs of the pictorial artist. In one sense it belongs entirely to prehistoric and ancient times, while in another sense it can be seen as ending with Leonardo.

The second major epoch of discovery belongs only to the past hundred years or so, and seems to have been motivated largely by the developing interest in the meaning of observation in science. The stimulation for the discovery of the remaining cues (and the intellectualization of a few of those previously discovered) came as a result of physicists' growing concern throughout the nineteenth century with the nature of observation. In any event, the rest of the cues of our list (excepting accommodation and convergence) date from the nineteenth century and were first mentioned by physicists. Helmholtz and Wheatstone share the distinction of rounding out the list of cues, notably with the specification of overlay, movement parallax, and binocular stereopsis.

The fact that accommodation and convergence do not belong to either of these two epochs is consistent with the anomalous position of these cues in the scientific study of space perception. As will be seen in Chapter VIII, there remains doubt as to whether they are properly to be included in the list of space cues. The relationship of both of these functions to space perception seems initially to have been postulated for opportunistic reasons; that is, by men who had discovered a principle in another connection and were interested in staking out as large as possible a claim for it. Euclid was the first to postulate convergence as a depth cue, and Kepler the first to espouse accommodation in that role. Accommodation and convergence are certainly related to space perception, but both men were incorrect in their initial claims.

CLASSIFICATION OF THE VISUAL SPACE CUES

The visual space cues have been classified by different writers in a variety of ways. But classification of concepts is relatively fruitless (as opposed to classification of observations which serves an important function in science), and most of the cue classifications are considered obsolete. Their residues, nevertheless, can be detected in enough contemporary writing to make their mention here appropriate. The cue classifications have tended to be in terms of a series of dichotomies, each carrying the implicit, though false, assumption that basically different processes are involved on the two sides of the dichotomy. The following is a representative list:

1. Monocular versus binocular
2. Psychological versus physiological
3. Secondary versus primary
4. Learned versus innate
5. Visual versus non-visual
6. Relative versus absolute

Although, on the surface, these six ways of dividing the visual cues seem to be quite different, they all represent more or less the same breakdown. Broadly speaking, and with some obvious exceptions, accommodation, convergence and binocular stereopsis belong to the second half of each pair, while all other cues fall into the first half.

FUNCTIONS OF THE VISUAL SPACE CUES

While classification of this kind has proved to be relatively useless, there are three more or less distinct functions served by the visual cues: *differentiation, identification* and *location*. These are separated for descriptive purposes only. In any concrete case all three are interrelated.

Differentiation. This is the function which Ames described as that of indicating "togetherness and apartness." Before there can be any visual space experience at all, there must be visual indications of certain partial togethernesses apart from other partial togethernesses. The visual cues most importantly involved in this function are color, brightness, light and shadow, relative movement, contour characteristics (sharpness of edge, coincidence of edge, overlay), double images, accommodation, and convergence.

Identification. Each differentiated partial togetherness is experienced as having its own particular object characteristics, or again in Ames' terms, a "thatness." Any particular experienced thatness is composed in part of meanings conveyed by subtle visual characteristics and in part of shape and solidity conveyed by visual cues such as light and shadow, stereopsis, shape, size, and perspective.

Location. Differentiated objects are experienced not only as possessing their own characteristics, but also their own locations in terms of distance and orientation, summarized in Ames' term "thereness." The more important cues involved here are size, overlay, position, stereopsis, perspective and parallax.

These three functions are completely interrelated in experience. Differentiation is a prerequisite for any visual space perception while thatness is never experienced except at some thereness and conversely. Similarly, these characteristics are not experienced abstractly, as they might be expressed in the language of physics, but rather as they function for the experiencing individual from his own personal behavioral center. Thatness and thereness can be expressed only in terms of the potential behavior of that individual, that is, operationally. Within any concrete transaction, the function served by the visual space cues then is to provide indications of the probable therenesses of the probable thatnesses of the various partial togethernesses from the personal behavioral center of the participant and in terms of his potential behaviors.

THE DEFINITION OF CUE

If we look at the list of cues carefully, it becomes clear that none of them is sufficiently sharply defined that its use becomes unequivocal. Rather, the listing is descriptive, each cue being identified so that the general meaning is more or less clear. This is an important and necessary first step, but it is far from final. The most obvious drawback to the descriptions is their lack of consistency. Some cues are described primarily in terms of the characteristics of the physical object, some in terms of the light energy, some with reference to physiological excitation and some entirely in terms of psychological factors. This heterogeneity is not accidental. It reflects a basic property of the cue concept. A cue is not something that can be pointed to; rather it represents a complex interrelationship between a number of aspects that must be taken into account in the definition of the cue.

If we examine the perceptual situation as we find it in concrete experience, we see that we are dealing with several relationships simultaneously. While we can isolate each aspect for study we must ultimately consider them as they actually operate in the perceptual process. Specifically, in discussing the visual depth cues we are primarily concerned with interrelationships among external objects, impinging light energy, physiological excitation and assumptions.

Externality-impingement relationships involve primarily physical optics and the geometry of Euclidean space. The question to be answered here is, what are the relationships between relevant characteristics of the impingement and relevant characteristics of the physical environment? (What is meant by the term "relevant" must here remain general.) The relevant aspects of the physical environment in so far as visual space perception is concerned are those aspects of the thereness and thatness, expressed in physical terms, which enter into, affect, or are affected by the participation of the individual. The relevant aspects of impingement are those which are related to the revelant aspects of the physical configuration.

The question of externality-impingement relationships is a double-barrelled one. First, given a particular physical configuration, what is the related impingement? This is the question, although not in these terms, which historically was asked first, as might be expected from a psychology which started off being concerned with what the environment does *to* the organism. However, Ames has shown that the question may more profitably, and more in keeping with a psychology interested in taking the organism as its central point, be asked in the other direction. Given a particular impingement, what are the related physical configurations? The implications of asking the question this way can scarcely be overestimated. It takes us from a rather mechanistic one-to-one causal connection to the recognition that from the standpoint of the active participant the relationship is not uniquely determined in advance of the concrete transaction. This result is expressed in the concept of *equivalent configurations*, i.e., from the standpoint of the active participant a number of physical configurations are equivalent with respect to impingement. The concept will be expanded in detail, following a brief discussion of the other two relationships.

Impingement-excitation relationships involve physiological optics, retinal physiology, the physiology of the optic nerve and central projection areas, the physics of light and related subjects. The exploration of this subject lies in the domain of physiological psychology and pure physiology. It starts with the impinging light—expressing in physical terms those aspects to which the receptor cells on the retina are sensitive. Beyond this, the impingement-excitation relationships include the whole area of nerve transmission and cortical activity in general. The most general question concerns the relationships between relevant characteristics of impingement and central neural activity, an area of inquiry which is outside the scope of this book. Of immediate relevance, however, is the fact that the answer to this general question cannot be given abstractly independent of the concrete situation. A variety of factors, specific to each particular situation, affect the relationship, such as sensory adaptation, fatigue, emotion, sympathetic activity and such physiological factors as vitamin deficiency and oxygen supply.

Excitation-assumption relationships involve inferred psychological variables. The question here asked is, under what conditions is a particular assumption related to a particular excitation? These relationships are quite variable. Assumptions as we have seen are derived from previous experiences, and since each person's experiences are to a certain extent unique, the excitation-assumption relationship necessarily differs from individual to individual. An extreme example of this might be assumptions about the characteristics of artifacts that are common in one culture and unknown in another. Similarly, the particular assumptions involved in any concrete perception depend not only on the excitation but also on psychological factors such as purpose, emotion, etc. In addition, there is a growing body of evidence which indicates that psychological activity is not simply a product of physiology but that there is a reciprocal relationship between the two.

To summarize, impingement, excitation and assumption in all their complex interrelationships enter concurrently into the transaction as "cue." They represent respectively the relevant physical, physiological and psychological aspects of the perceptual situation. The most important general conclusion that can be drawn about these relationships from the evidence to date is that none is determined uniquely in advance of the concrete transaction. We are not dealing with a unidirectional causal sequence going from object to impingement to excitation to psychological function. Rather we find that any impingement can be related to a large family of different objects, that any excitation can be the result of a large number of different impingements, and that psychological activity is not simply the product of physiological activity but that the two mutually affect each other.

The detailed analysis of the individual cues, which will be the subject matter of the following chapters, will emphasize externality-impingement relationships and the accompanying perceptions. What this reduces to quite specifically is the study of equivalent configurations and their related assumptions; each individual cue will be treated from this standpoint.

EQUIVALENT CONFIGURATIONS

Equivalent configurations are defined as that family of physical configurations for which impingement is invariant. Two configurations in the physical world can thus be defined as visually equivalent if they provide an observer with the same visual impingements. Conversely, a given impingement can be said to define two or more equivalent configurations if it can be shown that there exist two or more physical configurations that produce the same impingement. The proof of the existence of such equivalent configurations is primarily a problem in geometry. It is asserted here, and will be shown subsequently, that each of the visual cues defines an infinite family of equivalent configurations, or, to state the converse, for any cue there exists an infinite family of physical configurations, all of which provide the same visual cue.

From a functional point of view, it is essential, however, that the organism which receives these identical messages be able to distinguish between them. This can be done only on the basis of additional information from some other source which, as we shall see later, is provided in the form of assumptions.

There are two major considerations regarding equivalent configurations that will be of such importance throughout the remainder of this book that it may be well to point them out explicitly at the outset.

First, *the definition of equivalent configurations refers exclusively to physical variables,* and in itself says *nothing* about perception or any other psychological function.

Second, the definition of equivalent configurations implies that identical "incoming messages" can come from different external physical arrangements. *In the absence of other information, or if all other conditions remain constant, equivalent configurations will be perceived as identical,* no matter how different they may be physically.

The proof of the existence of a family of equivalent configurations related to any specific cue involves two steps:

1. The identification of the impingement aspects of the visual cue; this involves the specification of a particular characteristic of the impinging light rays which can be shown to be utilized in making distance discriminations.

2. The determination, usually by means of geometry, of the physical configurations which are adequate to account for any unique instance of the impingement aspect of the particular cue identified above. If these configurations are found to constitute an identifiable family then it can be stated that the particular visual cue defines a family of equivalent configurations.

The proof of the existence of equivalent configurations for an isolated distance cue does not constitute a generalized statement, however. In order to achieve generality two additional steps are needed.

3. Proof of the existence of equivalent configurations for *every* distance cue in isolation. As yet it is difficult to specify mathematically the exact characteristics of the impinging light energy which describe some of the cues. (In succeeding chapters this will be done in the light of present knowledge.) However, it seems reasonable to assume that, once this is done, equivalent configurations can be

derived for all cues with the possible exception of those which may be provided by accommodation and convergence innervations.

4. Following the proof of the existence of equivalent configurations for each isolated cue, the next step in generalization would consist of showing that various combinations of these cues do not result in a restriction of the freedom allowed by each cue individually. It can easily be shown, for example, that the combination of size and illumination results in no restriction, and a family of equivalent configurations can still be derived. Similar proofs for all possible combinations of cues could undoubtedly be worked out eventually. But such a procedure would be needlessly time-consuming, and a completely general proof seems required.

A general proof might be developed along the following lines; first, the proof that every cue or combination of cues can be expressed mathematically in terms of no more than two independent coordinates. Second, the proof that any statement in two independent coordinates must necessarily be ambiguous with respect to a third independent coordinate. While this general proof must await more accurate specification of all the cues, it seems reasonable to believe that it can eventually be provided. Until this can be done we shall simply assert, on the basis of the preceding discussion and the derivations of equivalent configurations which follow, that the visual distance cues are *always* ambiguous, in the sense that any combination of cues defines an infinite family of equivalent configurations which are indistinguishable one from another in their impingement aspects.

THE INVARIANCE HYPOTHESIS

We have thus far been concerned with relationships between externality and impingements. The translation of impingements into experience is a complex process involving many steps and many additional variables. The *invariance hypothesis* represents one simplified way of bridging this gap. It merits special discussion not only because it has been accepted, at least implicitly, by a wide variety of theorists, but also because it has considerable utility if properly applied and if its limitations are understood. This can only be accomplished by making them explicit.

Equivalent configurations involve statements of geometry. The invariance hypothesis states that this geometry can be translated directly into a description of psychological events. Specifically, the invariance hypothesis states that *with impingement invariant, perception must necessarily be of one of the equivalent configurations defined by that impingement.*

The way one progresses from impingement to perception via the invariance hypothesis is thus clear. Any given impingement defines a family of external physical configurations, any one of which might in fact be "out there." The perceptions possible under these conditions are limited, according to this hypothesis, exactly to this family of possible physical configurations. We may not know specifically which one is actually out there, and we may not know specifically which one will be perceived. But, following the invariance hypothesis, we do know that whatever is perceived will be exactly one of the equivalent configurations and nothing else.

This hypothesis has been utilized by psychologists in two ways. First, as *explanation*—some form of the invariance hypothesis is central to many theories of the *perceptual constancies.* As thus used, the most general statement of the invariance hypothesis holds that constancy depends on the existence of two processes which vary reciprocally so that the product always remains the same. This use of the invariance hypothesis will be treated in more detail when we are directly concerned with the separate cues.

At this point, we shall be concerned with the second major use of the invariance hypothesis, that of *description.* Is the invariance hypothesis adequate to describe the observed relationships as concretely encountered? The evidence relating to this question will be interspersed throughout the discussion to follow of the individual distance cues. The general conclusion will be stated here. First, the evidence is clear that the invariance hypothesis does describe the relationship as observed in many instances. As a principle, in the absence of contrary indications, one can safely assume the invariance hypothesis, at least as a first order approximation. This makes the hypothesis a very useful descriptive tool, *once it has been shown to apply.* Second, there are a sufficient number and variety of exceptions to the invariance hypothesis to make it clear that it is not *necessarily* applicable in a particular case. *It is never safe to assume arbitrarily that any given perception necessarily falls within the limits of the invariance hypothesis.* Perceptions drastically out of line with it can be observed. In summary, the invariance hypothesis sometimes but not necessarily describes the observed relationships. It loses, therefore, its status as an explanatory concept and becomes a description of results obtained under conditions which have not yet been completely specified.

This conclusion should not be surprising. The invariance hypothesis commonly represents an attempt to take a relationship derived under axioms of Euclidean geometry and to transfer it to the description of *psychological* events, although there is no *a priori* reason why this should be possible. When applied to *physical* objects in *physical* space and within certain limiting conditions, the invariance hypothesis is replaced by the statement of equivalent configurations which always holds. The concept of equivalent configurations is useful in psychology because it defines the physical limits of the experience of the organism. Whenever the organism meets with a particular impingement, this has always been produced by physical objects at physical distances uniquely specified by the appropriate equivalent configurations. The organism necessarily *encounters* one of the equivalent configurations. There have never been any exceptions to this rule; there never will be. When the invariance hypothesis adequately describes the reported perceptions, this simply means that the perceptions most nearly approximate the physical situations which have been related to all the relevant experience of the organism and which are summarized by the statement of equivalent configurations.

Perceptions which meet this criterion can be subsumed under the general label of *perceptual invariance*. It may be well, therefore, to define this term and compare it with the more usual term of perceptual constancy.

Perceptual invariance refers to the case in which perception corresponds to a physical configuration which might produce the impingement (i.e., one of the equivalent configurations).

Perceptual constancy refers to the case in which perception corresponds to the particular physical configuration which in the specific case actually produced the impingement.

Perceptual non-invariance refers to the case in which perception corresponds to a physical configuration which could not have produced the impingement (i.e., not one of the equivalent configurations).

Just as in the case of constancy, there can be degrees of invariance. Constancy experiments have not, in general, drawn a sharp dividing line between constancy and non-constancy, but have rather introduced quantitative measures (e.g., the constancy ratio) of the degree of constancy. Similarly, although they have not as yet been conducted, an analogous set of invariance experiments might profitably be carried out using some similar measure of quantitative departure from perfect invariance. The term non-invariance would then be reserved for a clear-cut qualitative discrepancy and perhaps also extreme quantitative deviations.

Perceptual invariance is a more inclusive term than constancy, which can be subsumed under it as a special case. Perceptual constancy is, by definition, also perceptual invariance. However, even extreme departures from constancy need not, and usually do not, represent any deviation from invariance. Unfortunately, the great bulk of the constancy experiments which have shown deviations from constancy do not present sufficient data to evaluate the relation of the deviations to invariance.

The conditions under which perceptual invariance can be obtained have yet to be determined, but should provide a more satisfactory base line for evaluating experimental results than the criterion of constancy. Deviations from constancy represent a discrepancy between perception and the immediate situation. Deviations from invariance represent a denial of the sum total of all actual and possible experiences of the individual.

THE SIZE-DISTANCE INVARIANCE HYPOTHESIS

Extremely common in the literature of visual space perception are explanations or descriptions of the relationship between size, distance and visual angle which resort to the use of mathematical expressions which are special cases of the proportions existing in similar triangles. Such applications of Euclidean plane geometry to psychological relationships, with their consequent (often uncritical) mixture of physical and psychological variables, offer attractively simple solutions. They also represent perhaps the most common illustrations of the use, and misuse, of the invariance hypothesis. The value of these solutions rests on the degree to which they are consistent with the observed relationships. Consequently, a careful scrutiny of the solutions in relation to the experimental evidence would seem to be in order.

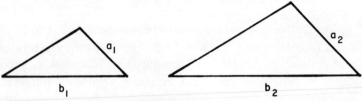

Figure IV-I The geometry of similar triangles underlies the size-distance invariance hypothesis.

The basic expression of the size-distance invariance hypothesis follows directly from an elementary theorem of plane geometry. The proportions between corresponding parts of similar triangles shown in Figure IV-1 can be expressed as

$$\frac{a_1}{b_1} = \frac{a_2}{b_2}.$$

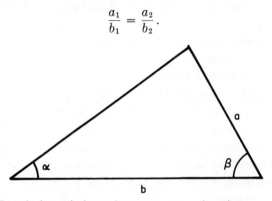

Figure IV-2 Triangle from which size-distance invariance hypothesis can be derived.

It follows directly from this that specifying α (Figure IV-2) determines the relationship between a, b, and β. Specifically, this relationship is given by

$$\tan \alpha = \frac{a \sin \beta}{b - a \cos \beta}. \qquad \text{IV-1}$$

We can apply this simple geometry to physical objects in physical space, if we confine ourselves to sizes and distances which are neither too small nor too large.

Let S be the physical size of an object (Figure IV-3) at a physical distance D from some reference point, let α be the angle subtended by S, and let δ be the deviation of S from the vertical, or the *inclination* of S. Equation IV-1 becomes

$$\tan \alpha = \frac{S \cos \delta}{D - S \sin \delta}. \qquad \text{IV-2}$$

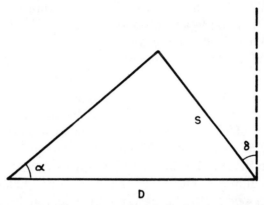

Figure IV-3 At distance D an object of size S at slant δ subtends visual angle α.

If we limit ourselves to angles sufficiently small so tan α = α, which implies that D is very much larger than S, and consider as a special case the condition δ = O (Figure IV-4), Equation IV-2 reduces to

$$\alpha = \frac{S}{D}.$$

IV–3

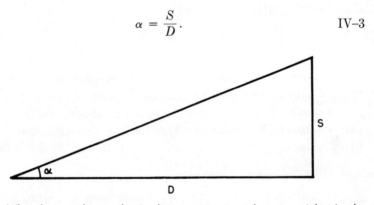

Figure IV-4 When slant equals zero, the size-distance geometry reduces to a right triangle.

In this chapter we shall consider the implications only of Equation IV-3, bearing in mind at all times that it is only a special case of Equation IV-2, which is in turn a special case of the three-dimensional relationship, including the most general case in which S is a curved surface.

Certain simple conclusions may be drawn from the relationship between visual angle, size and distance.

a. When the angle is given, size and distance vary proportionally.
b. When angle and distance are given, size is uniquely defined.
c. When angle and size are given, distance is uniquely defined.
d. When size is given, angle and distance vary inversely.
e. When distance is given, angle and size vary proportionally.

This simple geometry of the right triangle is of interest to the student of space perception because the apparent sizes and apparent distances of objects seem to conform to similar or identical rules. Indeed, in many cases Equation IV-3 seems quite accurately to describe the relationship between apparent size, apparent distance, and visual angle. This fact has led some psychologists to apply this equation bodily to the description of psychological events. At its most naive, such an approach leads to equations that uncritically mingle physical and psychological quantities such as

$$\text{visual angle} = \frac{\text{apparent size}}{\text{physical distance}}$$

while at its most sophisticated the same net result is expressed slightly differently in the form

$$\text{retinal size} = K \frac{\text{apparent size}}{\text{apparent distance}}.$$

However stated, one assumption is central to all such applications of simple geometry to perceived space: *A retinal projection or visual angle of given size determines a unique ratio of apparent size to apparent distance.* This is the size-distance invariance hypothesis.

Supporting experimental evidence

As *explanation,* we have seen, some form of invariance hypothesis is central to many theories of the perceptual constancies. This type of explanation as related to the size-distance problem was first proposed by Wheatstone; it is central in the Gestalt theory of constancy, implied in much of Boring's writing, and again crucial and explicit in Gibson's theory, to mention a few important examples. However, at this point we will be concerned only with the use of the invariance hypothesis as *description.* Is the invariance hypothesis adequate to describe the observed relationships between apparent size, apparent distance and visual angle?

It is well attested that the hypothesis does describe this relationship in many instances, and no attempt will be made here to survey the literature on the subject systematically. Rather we will indicate the general nature of the supporting evidence. Three cases may profitably be distinguished.

1. *Visual angle constant.* The invariance hypothesis demands that apparent size and apparent distance vary proportionally, and indeed this is the most commonly reported result. Duke-Elder has summarized the current evidence of this case by noting that, "If we estimate the distance to be much greater than it is, we consider that if the object at this distance is so big, it must be very big indeed. Conversely, if an object seems nearer than it is, it seems to be smaller than it actually is." This case is also the one with which Emmert's law is concerned, the usual interpretation of which is in support of the invariance hypothesis.

2. *Apparent distance constant.* The invariance hypothesis demands that apparent size vary directly with visual angle, and again this is the most commonly reported result. This case is, in fact, closely related to the finding of most size-constancy work that the proper estimation of size is dependent upon the proper estimation of distance.

3. *Apparent size constant.* The invariance hypothesis demands that apparent distance vary inversely with visual angle. This general finding has been repeatedly verified in a variety of cases.

It is clear, then, that considerable experimental evidence can be mustered in support of the invariance hypothesis, and indeed most writers on the problem of the relation between apparent size and apparent distance would seem to be in general agreement with this hypothesis. The prevailing view can be summarized in the words of Sanford written over half a century ago, "Size and distance are mutually determining. If the apparent distance is constant, the apparent size of the objects changes directly with the size of the retinal image; while if the apparent size is constant, the apparent distance changes inversely with the image. These are facts of very common observation."

Contradictory experimental evidence

Not all the relevant experimental evidence is in such unequivocal support of the invariance hypothesis. The contradictory evidence,

which is scattered and possibly not conclusive, stems from a variety
of experimental approaches.

1. *Varying accommodation while looking at a fixed object.*
The relation between accommodation and apparent size under these
conditions is well established. Anyone can verify for himself the
truth of Hering's report that, "When changing from a monocular
fixation of a distant object to viewing one close by, the distant object
appears to diminish in size. Conversely, the size of the nearer object
increases when accommodating for the farther." The relation of this
effect to apparent distance is by no means so clearly established.
This problem has never been systematically investigated, but it has
been mentioned by many writers who, although they are not in
complete agreement, would seem to support von Kries in stating:

"When we gaze at any object with one eye screened, it is easy
to notice that its apparent size varies with the state of accommodation. Every exertion of accommodation is accompanied by an apparent reduction in size, and every relaxation by an apparent magnification. The simplest explanation of this well-known and easily
observed phenomenon would be to suppose that as the result of
accommodation for near vision the object appears to be at the distance that ordinarily corresponds to this accommodation, that is,
too near; and hence, as long as it subtended the same visual angle,
its absolute size would appear to be less than it was. The trouble
about this explanation is that, as Donders long ago rightly pointed
out as something remarkable, this is not what actually happens. The
object does appear to become smaller when accommodation is
exerted, but it by no means appears to come nearer at the same
time; on the contrary it appears to recede. Thus, with a constant
visual angle, we see here apparent size and apparent distance vary
in the opposite sense."

This is clearly in contradiction to the invariance hypothesis.
It should, however, be pointed out that this evidence, as well as
that in the following section, is complicated by the possibility that
the physical size of the retinal projection varies with changes of
accommodation.

2. *Accommodative micropsia due to partial paralysis of accommodation.* Partial paralysis of accommodation, most commonly by
means of atropine, is accompanied by a reduction in apparent size,
or micropsia. While this fact is well established, the relation to

apparent distance again is not completely clear. Duke-Elder implicitly attributes this effect to the invariance hypothesis when he writes that, "In partial paralysis of accommodation . . . we volitionally expend a greater effort to see an object distinctly . . . and we thus imagine the object to be quite near; but since the retinal image is of the same size, we think the object must be smaller than it is." Hering, however, reported findings of Aubert which specifically refute this explanation. "Aubert, after instillation of 1/500 grain atropine, saw letters with the atropinized eye at a distance of 20 feet, apparently half the size as seen with the other . . . In spite of this, strange to say, the apparently smaller objects did not seem nearer but farther than in the sound eye." This report is clearly in contradiction to the invariance hypothesis.

3. *Visual tau effect.* "If three discrete points of light are successively presented, and the distance between the points of light is equal, but the time interval between the first and second points of light is greater (lesser) than the time interval between the second and third, then the perceived space between the first and second will be greater (lesser) than the perceived space between the second and third points of light" (Helson & King). Contrary to what one might expect in terms of the invariance hypothesis, there is no evidence that this well-attested phenomenon is accompanied by any apparent distance change. Of course, it might be argued that the perceived space between the successively presented lights is not "size" in the usual sense, as the lights which set the space limits do not stimulate the retina simultaneously. Nevertheless, pending further experimentation, the visual tau effect might reasonably be considered an exception to the invariance hypothesis.

4. *Subjective factors.* Recent evidence stemming from personality-oriented investigations indicates that the apparent size of an object may be influenced by subjective factors such as the importance of the object to the observer, which may constitute a significant exception to the invariance hypothesis.

5. *Invariance experiments.* Two experiments have been reported whose chief objective was to test the invariance hypothesis. Ittelson and Kilpatrick presented objects of constant size and distance moving through a field which offered varying and conflicting indications of size and distance. Out of 96 judgments, they obtained 49 which were in accord with the invariance hypothesis and 47

which were not. Gruber, in a quantitative study, obtained both size and distance judgments of two similar triangles. The apparent distances reported by his subjects not only did not agree with the distances predicted by the invariance hypothesis from the previously obtained size judgments, but went in the opposite direction. He labeled this finding the "size-distance paradox." Both of these experiments reported perceptual non-invariance.

6. *Statistical considerations.* Much if not all of the evidence which tends to support the invariance hypothesis is statistical in nature; it states that the invariance hypothesis describes the mean of a large number of observations in a large number of cases. But, as usually expressed, the invariance hypothesis is not a statistical statement; it is an equation which, within the limits of accuracy of measurement, must apply to the individual case. Therefore, even if the invariance hypothesis always adequately described the mean performance (which, as we have seen, it does not), it would still have to be modified drastically before it would be acceptable as a description of psychological events.

The size-distance invariance hypothesis is commonly expressed in the form

$$\text{visual angle} = \frac{\text{apparent size}}{\text{apparent distance}} \qquad [\text{IV–4}]$$

or some equation reducible to this. Such equations represent an attempt to take a relation derived under the axioms of Euclidean plane geometry and to transfer it bodily to the description of psychological events. There is no *a priori* reason why this should be possible.

When applied to physical space, and within certain limiting conditions, the equation

$$\alpha = \frac{\text{physical size}}{\text{physical distance}} \qquad [\text{IV–5}]$$

always holds. As we have seen, this equation is useful to the psychologist because it defines the physical limits of the experience of the organism. Whenever the retina is stimulated along a length describable by the visual angle α, this is always produced by physical objects at physical distances uniquely specified by the above equation (or more generally by Equation IV-2). When Equation IV-4 adequately describes the reported perceptions, this simply means that the perceptions most nearly approximate the physical situations which have been related to all the size-distance experience of the organism, and which can be summarized by Equation IV-5. We have, in other words, an example of perceptual size-distance invariance. This is a common, but by no means necessary, mode of perceiving.

V

Size,
Shape,
Perspective

Any starting point in the discussion of individual space cues must to a certain extent be arbitrary since the isolation of the individual cues is itself arbitrary. Never in normal experience is an observer presented with a visual situation in which one and only one cue is operative, and to achieve such a condition even in the laboratory presents one of the most difficult technical problems in the experimental study of the space cues. But since we can only talk about one thing at a time, the cues must be, and traditionally are, separated for purposes of discussion.

We will first discuss size and distance and their interrelationships, and then turn to shape, slant and distance. Finally the relationship of these cues to perspective will be pointed out. No full discussion of perspective will be presented here since the geometry of perspective is covered in numerous excellent references; rather, we will be concerned with some specific problems of perspective which follow from the study of the size and shape cues and which point up psychological implications.

Size, shape and perspective are chosen to open our study of the space cues for a variety of reasons. They belong to the group of cues which have been classified as monocular, that is, they do not depend on the use of the two eyes. The geometry of these cues, especially of size, is considerably simpler than that of the binocular cues. Furthermore, these cues are among the major cues accounting for our visual space perceptions. Most important, they nicely and simply illustrate all of the important aspects involved in the study of space perception, many of which can be seen only obscurely and with difficulty in the other cues.

SIZE AND DISTANCE

As we have already seen in the preceding chapter, size and distance vary reciprocally. Objects which approach seem to get bigger, objects which recede seem to get smaller. On the other hand, if an object is seen closer than it actually is, it is seen small, while if it is seen farther away than it actually is, it is seen large. This reciprocal relationship results in two somewhat different aspects to the size-distance problem. These can be differentiated as (1) size determined by distance, and (2) distance determined by size. Both of these problems were discovered and dealt with at approximately the same time in history. In the second century, Ptolemy wrote about apparent size and the moon illusion, which has historically been interpreted as a question of size determined by distance; while in Pompeii (destroyed in 79 A.D.) we have the first unequivocal examples of the use of perspective, which is an aspect of distance determined by size.

Through history, however, these two problems have been treated as if they were unrelated. The greater part of writing and experimentation has been devoted to the problem of size as determined by distance. Starting with Ptolemy, the converse problem has been neglected, and a gradual trend toward considering distance as primary and size secondary ultimately leads to the complete denial of the problem that size may be a determinant of distance. An example of this extreme view is provided by Boring. "When no relevant datum other than retinal size is available, then the perception of size will, after all, vary solely with the visual angle; this is a tautology and must be true." This may be a tautology but it does not happen to be true. The evidence is clear, as we shall shortly see, that under these conditions the perception of *distance* is just as likely to vary with visual angle.

That the problem of distance as determined by size has been neglected is probably due to the greater importance of size-constancy in everyday living. Correct size perceptions are functionally essential, while size as a distance cue is only one of many. This probably also accounts for the lack of the use of size as a cue to distance in much primitive and children's art as well as distortions in more sophisticated art; that is, the attempt is made to present things as they look, and distant objects do not necessarily look smaller than near objects. A striking illustration is in the comparison of a photograph of a distant mountain, the actual view of the mountain, and an artist's rendition of it. The majestic, towering mountain appears as an insignificant bump on the horizon of the photograph, whereas the artist can exaggerate in one way or another to convey the experience of seeing a mountain. Whatever the reasons for the neglect of size as a cue to distance, the fact remains that perspective, which first appeared about the first century, was fully developed in the 12th century and represents an entirely separate line of development from the problem of apparent size. The question of the size cue as such appears much later. In the 19th century Wheatstone refers to continuous size-change, and Helmholtz to familiar size and indirectly to relative size; but neither refers to any earlier work. It is not until the second half of the 19th century that we find all three aspects explicitly stated, namely, absolute size, relative size and changing size. But up to the present day, size as determined by distance and distance as determined by size continue to be treated by most writers as if they were unrelated problems.

All three aspects of size as a cue to distance together with the much older problem of apparent size as a function of distance will form the subject matter of our analysis.

Size-equivalent configurations

The particular characteristics of externality with which we are here concerned are the physical size, slant, and distance of objects. The impingement characteristics are those which determine the size of the retinal area stimulated which we can specify in terms of visual angle, i.e., the angle subtended at the nodal point of the eye by the physical object in question. (The equating of visual angle to retinal size is not rigorous, of course, but is adequate for the present purpose and greatly simplifies the discussion.) In the case of absolute size we are concerned with a single angle, in the case of relative size with the ratio between two or more visual angles, and in the case of dynamic size change with continuous change in visual angle.

Figure V-1, taken from Bartley, illustrates the general principle of size-equivalent configurations in that it shows a number of different objects of different sizes and slants, all of which subtend the same visual angle. It is relatively simple to arrive at a mathematical expression of the principle illustrated in this figure if for the sake

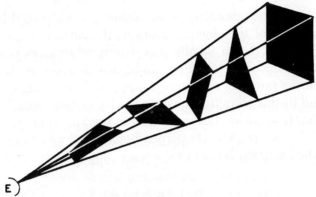

Figure V-1 Size-equivalent configurations (after Bartley).

of simplicity we consider only a single plane passing through the
nodal point of the eye. Figure V-1 then reduces to Figure V-2 which
illustrates some of the family of size equivalent configurations
defined by the visual angle α.

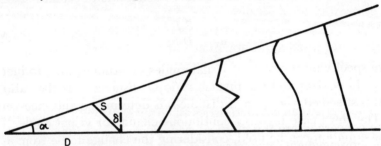

Figure V-2 Special case of size-equivalent configurations lying in plane passing through
the eye.

If we further limit our discussion to plane surfaces, as we have
seen in the preceding chapter the equation

$$\tan \alpha = \frac{S \cos \delta}{D - S \sin \delta} \qquad \text{V–1}$$

specifies the entire family using the vertical to the line of sight as a
reference. It is possible but not particularly useful for the present
discussion to generalize this equation for a fixed reference system
independent to the observer and for curved as well as plane surfaces.

Any surface which satisfies Equation V-1 provides exactly the
same size cue, specified by α, as does any other surface which satis-

fies this equation. Similarly if the value of α is changed by changing one or more of the characteristics of the surface, e.g., its distance, slant, or size, then a wholly new family of surfaces is defined, the characteristics of which can again be determined from Equation V-1.

For the purposes of discussion and without losing generality, we can still further simplify Equation V-1 by limiting ourselves to angles sufficiently small so that tan $\alpha = \alpha$ and considering only the case in which $\delta = 0$, i.e., objects perpendicular to the line of sight. In this case the equation reduces to

$$\alpha = \frac{S}{D}. \qquad\qquad \text{V-2}$$

It is clear from this equation that holding visual angle invariant defines a family of surfaces whose physical size and physical distance vary proportionately. Specifying the size uniquely determines the distance, and specifying the distance uniquely determines the size.

Used for the case of relative size, the equation becomes

$$\frac{\alpha_1}{\alpha_2} = \frac{S_1 D_2}{D_1 S_2}. \qquad\qquad \text{V-3}$$

Here specifying the ratio of visual angles determines the product òf the ratio of sizes and the inverse ratio of distances. If the ratio of sizes is specified, the ratio of distances is determined and vice-versa.

The third case involves continuous change of visual angle. The same equation can be used, considering the change to be from α_1 to α_2. If size remains constant

$$\frac{\alpha_1}{\alpha_2} = S\frac{D_2}{D_1},$$

and the object moves from D_1 to D_2 in such a way that if the visual angle increases, the distance decreases and vice-versa. This is a statement of the familiar fact that as a constant-size object approaches, it subtends a larger visual angle.

At the other extreme, distance can remain constant, in which event size varies directly with visual angle. Any combination of change of size and change of distance within these extremes satisfies the requirements for equivalent configurations under conditions of change in visual angle.

Size assumptions

For the purposes of this discussion we will assume that the invariance hypothesis holds. This means that we can substitute apparent size and apparent distance for the physical size and physical distance of Equation V-2, giving us

$$\alpha = K \frac{\text{apparent size}}{\text{apparent distance}}.$$

As mentioned earlier, great care must be exercised in using this hypothesis. It holds only under restricted conditions and only to first order approximation. We have already described cases in which the size-distance invariance hypothesis breaks down.

Within the context of the invariance hypothesis, however, as expressed in the above equation, the following points are clear:

Absolute size.   For a given visual angle, assuming the physical size determines the apparent distance. The larger the assumed size the farther away the object appears; the smaller the assumed size the nearer the object appears.

Relative size.   For a given ratio of visual angles, assuming the ratio of physical sizes determines the ratio of distances. If the assumed sizes are equal, the object subtending the larger visual angle appears nearer and the one subtending the smaller appears farther.

Radial motion.   With visual angle continuously changing, if the object is assumed to be of constant size, apparent distance changes inversely with visual angle. That is, as its visual angle increases, the object appears to move directly toward the observer and vice-versa.

Apparent size and size-constancy.   For a given visual angle, if apparent distance is assumed, apparent size is given. Size-constancy, i.e., apparent size equal to physical size, will be achieved if assumed size equals physical size, or if assumed distance equals physical distance. In general, however, these are trivial cases in the study of size-constancy, which is usually studied in situations in which other distance cues are present.

Empirical facts of the size-distance relationship

In general, the findings with respect to the size-distance relationship follow the limits of the invariance hypothesis; that is, the state-

ments in the preceding section have in general been empirically
borne out.

1. *Absolute size as a cue to absolute distance.*   Under conditions of monocular observation in a dark room, i.e., where size is
the only or at least the major cue operative, a single object, however
unfamiliar or ambiguous, is always seen localized at a definite and
unequivocal apparent distance. The particular distance at which the
object is seen depends on assumptions as to that distance (Jastrow,
Bourdon, Ames) or as to its physical size (Ames, Hastorf, Lawrence,
Ittelson, Ittelson and Ames, W. Smith). With unfamiliar objects
the apparent distance has been shown to depend on (1) expected
distance derived from a knowledge of the surroundings (Jastrow,
Bourdon, Ames); (2) assumed size derived from the size of other
objects in the field (Ittelson); (3) assumed size derived from generalized experience with objects of the same general nature (Ames,
Ittelson); or (4) suggestions of assumed size (Hastorf). With
familiar objects the apparent distance is determined by the assumed
(familiar) size derived from generalized life experience (Ames,
Ittelson, Lawrence, Hastorf) or from specific controlled experimental experience (W. Smith). The assumed size of familiar objects
has been shown by Slack to be effective even in the presence of
many conflicting cues. Assumed size and apparent distance are
further influenced by emotions, needs, purposes and so forth; this is
treated in more detail in Chapter X.

2. *Relative size as a cue to relative distance.*   Under conditions
of monocular observation in a dark room, two similar objects will be
seen at relative distances inversely proportional to the visual angles
subtended. The one subtending the larger visual angle will appear
closer than the one subtending the smaller visual angle in such a
way that their apparent sizes appear equal (Ames, Bourdon, Peter,
Bappert, Pouillard, Petermann, Carr, Ittelson, Hochberg). Ames has
accounted for this general fact by referring to the assumption that
"similar things are identical" which the observer will always make
in the absence of other evidence.

If the two objects are not similar their relative distances will
depend on the ratio of their visual angles and the ratio of their
assumed sizes. The latter may be derived from any of the sources
described in the case of absolute size as a cue to absolute distance.
For example, if one object subtends a small visual angle but is

assumed to be very small physically, it may appear nearer than an object which subtends a larger visual angle but is assumed to be very large (Ames, Ittelson). Similarly, of two objects subtending equal visual angles, the one assumed smaller will be seen near while the one assumed larger will be seen farther.

This latter effect can probably best be conceptualized as a case of cue-conflict (cf. Chapter IX). Relative size has been studied in conflict with absolute size (Ames, Ittelson, Hochberg), binocular disparity (Hirsch, Vernon, Ittelson, Ames, Schriever, Wheatstone), color (Leventhal), parallax, overlay, etc.

3. *Changing size as a cue to radial motion.* Under conditions of monocular observation in a dark room, continuous change of the visual angle subtended by an object is perceived as continuous movement in space. As the visual angle increases, the object appears to approach in such a way as to maintain constant apparent size (Wheatstone, Hillebrand, Ames, Calavrezo, Bartley, Metzger, Hastorf, Ittelson, Kilpatrick and Ittelson, W. Smith). The apparent direction of this movement is directly toward or away from the observer, hence the name *radial motion.* Apparent radial motion resulting from continuous change of visual angle is indistinguishable from objective radial motion (Ittelson). The ratio of the apparent near point of travel to the apparent far point of travel depends on the ratio of the visual angles but is not completely determined by it since individual differences exist in the tendency to inhibit or encourage movement. The apparent distance of travel of radial movement resulting from continuous size change depends on the specific apparent radial localization of the perceived object which, as we have seen, depends in turn on the assumed size of the object. The threshold of radial motion has been studied as a function of object dimensionality, object meaning and other factors (W. Smith).

Apparent radial motion has been studied in conflict with binocular disparity (Ittelson, W. Smith), and in general has been found to override disparity. It is one of the most important cues to movement in depth in motion pictures and television. In line with the preceding evidence, it seems probable that the critical factor here is an assumption that the physical size of an object remains constant, although a definitive test of this hypothesis is still lacking.

4. *Apparent size and size constancy.* The problem of apparent size within the context of the invariance hypothesis is in one sense

the opposite of that of size as a cue to distance. In the latter we are concerned with apparent distance as determined by visual angle and size-assumptions, in the former we are concerned with apparent size as a function of visual angle and apparent distance. The findings in general are consistent; apparent size is determined by apparent distance in accordance with the invariance hypothesis. If apparent distance approximates physical distance, apparent size will approximate physical size (i.e., size constancy). In general, the more depth cues operative, the closer apparent size is to physical size and hence to size-constancy.

If size is the *only cue* present, distance may be assumed, which will then determine size, which is the inverse of the problem of assumed size determining distance, already discussed. In the more general case, apparent distance is determined at least in part by other cues and, therefore, determines apparent size. Yet, in principle, there is no basis for assuming the primacy of distance over size as many authors do.

The literature on size constancy is adequately summarized in a number of sources, and this work will not be duplicated here. For the present discussion it is important to note that the study of size constancy has tended to be separated into two problems: first, size constancy as a function of distance cues and, second, size constancy as a function of a variety of other factors.

With respect to distance cues this general finding has already been indicated. It is frequently expressed by saying that apparent size represents a compromise between retinal size and real size. Such a statement has no meaning, however, since neither "retinal size" nor "real size" is expressible in the same units as apparent size. This is, in fact, none other than the question considered in the previous chapter. What the statement is intended to describe is a situation in which two objects are equated for apparent size. In the absence of other distance cues, correct prediction can be made from a knowledge of the visual angles. With full distance cues, correct prediction can be made from a knowledge of the physical sizes. In most cases the actual match falls in between these two limits. Very important exceptions to this rule have already been indicated, and it is at best an empirical generalization from a limited number of experiments conducted under very special circumstances.

The importance of the conditions under which size constancy

experiments are conducted is attested by the number of experiments dealing with factors other than distance cues *per se*. Such variables as the direction of observation, the distance of observation, illumination and angular separation are still fairly obviously related to visual functioning. Other variables, with no direct visual reference, have also introduced important effects, notably the mode of observation (variously described as analytic vs. naive, look vs. bet, etc.), the subjective significance of the object to the observer, and the general personality characteristics of the observer. The fact that all these factors importantly influence apparent size serves to underline the importance of a complete re-evaluation of size constancy as part of the over-all functioning of the individual along the lines indicated in the previous chapters.

Most apparent size experiments provide measures of apparent size and physical size but not of apparent distance. Hence, in general, we have enough data to measure size-constancy but not enough to determine whether the size-distance invariance hypothesis holds. Many of the findings which are discussed in terms of field structure, and Gestalt factors, or in terms of illumination, separation and so forth may simply be subsumed under the invariance hypothesis. Others may clearly represent examples of failure of the invariance hypothesis to hold. However, such conclusions remain speculative.

SHAPE

The question of the shape-distance relationship is very closely allied with that of size. Indeed, size could be treated independently of shape only by quite drastically limiting the generality of the discussion. This intimate relationship can be illustrated by reference to one of the simplest size experiments, Ames' line demonstration. If we connect the two lines of Figure V-3 as in Figure V-4 we have shape and perspective simultaneously.

The study of shape forces us to consider a fact which we arbitrarily omitted in the discussion of size, namely slant. We are always dealing with shape at a slant at a distance. Historically, this has been more frequently ignored than recognized. The overwhelming majority of studies dealing with this general area have been concerned with the apparent shape of paper-and-pencil drawings. They have thereby ruled out both distance and slant from consideration in a topic rather arbitrarily labeled *form perception*, as differentiated

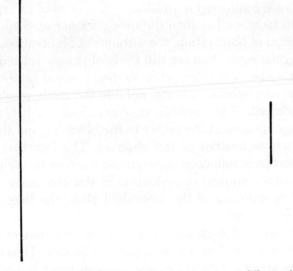

Figure V-3   Two lines of different relative sizes are seen at different distances.

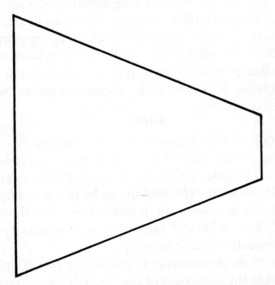

Figure V-4   Relative size becomes shape by adding two lines.

from a separate subject matter, depth perception. Such a distinction, however, is arbitrary and would seem to have no theoretical or logical justification. Two-dimensional form perception can most properly be considered a special case of three-dimensional depth perception rather than the reverse. Since almost any plane figure has some apparent depth, it remains a moot question what to label such an apparently three-dimensional, physically two-dimensional object. Even when a physically two-dimensional, apparently two-dimensional form is achieved, we are dealing with the case in which apparent slant equals zero.

The bulk of the work on shape which we will be concerned has been devoted to shape-constancy in the shape-slant relationship. Very little work has been devoted to shape-constancy as a function of distance, and still less to the general problem of shape at a slant at a distance. But if this general problem of apparent shape and shape-constancy has been slighted in favor of more restricted studies, the related problem of shape as a cue to distance has been virtually ignored. Nevertheless, as Gibson has been at pains to point out, the apparent shape and slant of the surfaces about us is very closely interrelated with apparent depth. Shape functions as a cue to distance indirectly—shape being a cue to absolute slant, relative shape a cue to relative slant, and changing shape a cue to changing slant.

Shape-equivalent configurations

Any general equation for shape-equivalent configurations would depend on some specification of the general impingement characteristics related to shape. Such a broad specification would be difficult to derive and has not as yet been worked out; in practice equations are separately derived for each particular case. The two shape-equivalent configurations most commonly studied are represented by the rectangle-trapezoid and the circle-ellipse families.

Any given impingement, whose shape can loosely be described as trapezoidal, can be produced by a series of rectangles at different distances and slants and also by a series of trapezoids at different distances and slants.

The same general statements hold for the circle-ellipse family and can more easily be shown mathematically. If we specify a horizontal visual angle β and a vertical visual angle 2α, β can be considered the impingement of the horizontal axis of an ellipse and 2α the impingement of the vertical axis. Limiting ourselves to small angles and to the case in which the horizontal axis is at right angles to the line of sight, we have the horizontal axis, b, given by Equation V-4 where d is the distance to the center of the ellipse.

$$b = \beta d \qquad\qquad \text{V-4}$$

Similarly, referring to Figure V-5, the vertical axis, a, is given by Equation V-5

$$\alpha = \frac{\frac{a}{2}\cos\delta}{d - \frac{a}{2}\sin\delta} \qquad\qquad \text{V-5}$$

which reduces to Equation V-6, assuming that d is very much larger than a,

$$2\alpha = \frac{a\cos\delta}{d}. \qquad\qquad \text{V-6}$$

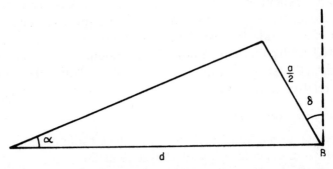

Figure V-5   Cross-section through an ellipse at slant δ. The ellipse has a vertical axis a and a horizontal axis b (at right angles to the figure through point B).

The shape of the ellipse can be completely specified by the ratio of its two principal axes, given by Equation V-7.

$$\frac{2\alpha}{\beta} = \frac{a\cos\delta}{b} \qquad\qquad \text{V-7}$$

From this equation we see that any given impinging ellipse, specified by 2α and β, determines a family of ellipses at different slants. The relation between the shape of any one of these ellipses and its slant is given by the equation and is independent of distance. The condition for the special case in which the equivalent configuration is a circle is given by

$$\frac{a}{b} = 1 .$$

A simple extension of the above derivation applied to the trapezoid illustrated in Figure V-6 gives us the ratio of b_1 to b_2 by Equation V-8 again assuming that the viewing distance is very much larger than a or b,

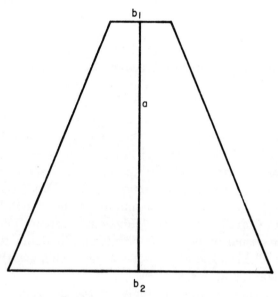

Figure V-6   A trapezoidal shape can be specified by a vertical dimension a and two horizontal dimensions b_1 and $b_{2'}$.

$$\frac{b_1}{b_2} = \frac{\beta_1}{\beta_2} \qquad\qquad\text{V-8}$$

and the ratio of b_1 to a by Equation V-9.

$$\frac{b_1}{a} = \frac{\beta_1}{\alpha} \cos \delta \qquad\qquad\text{V-9}$$

These two ratios specify the trapezoid. Here again we find that for a given trapezoidal impingement, specified by α, β_1 and β_2, a family of trapezoids at different slants is determined. Again this family is independent of distance, for large viewing distances. As the distance decreases, it enters into the more general equations as a second order term. The special case in which the equivalent configuration is a rectangle is given by the condition $\frac{b_1}{b_2} = 1$, while for a square the restriction $\frac{b_1}{a} = 1$ is added.

It should be pointed out that, while the shape of the impingement can be described in terms of a ratio of visual angles, e.g., for the ellipse $\frac{2\alpha}{\beta}$, the equivalent configurations determined by the impingement depend not only on its shape but also on the absolute magnitude of the angles involved. Therefore, specifying the shape of the impingement is not sufficient to determine the family of shape-equivalent configurations. The absolute values of the visual angles must also be given.

We can summarize the major characteristics of shape-equivalent configurations. Any given impingement of a specified shape determines a family of external configurations of differing shapes and slants. In general, the more the shape of the external configuration differs from the impinging shape, the greater will be its slant. The shape-equivalent configurations thus determined are independent of distance. That is, the identical family is duplicated at every distance. However, within this family shape and slant are mutually dependent, and specifying one uniquely determines the other.

Specifying the shape of the impingement is not sufficient to determine the family of shape-equivalent configurations. The size, expressed in visual angle, must be given. Changing the size, i.e., multiplying all visual angles by a constant, changes the family of equivalent configurations.

It is clear that, within the limits of the invariance hypothesis:

1. Assuming shape determines this shape at a unique slant but indeterminate distance.

2. Assuming slant determines a unique shape at this slant again with distance indeterminate.

3. Adding assumptions as to size uniquely determines the distance.

Empirical facts of shape-slant-distance relationship

Not a great deal of experimentation has been done that is directly relevant to the preceding discussion. Considerably more has been done with the more limited aspect of shape constancy. Since this is amply covered in standard references (Vernon, Woodworth and Schlossberg, Osgood) it will not be summarized here. There are only a few studies dealing directly with shape-slant relationships and fewer still adding distance considerations.

Gibson has been most prominent in studying the role of slant in relation to distance. He has been concerned primarily with textural cues to slant rather than with shape *per se*. However, his work indicates that the apparent slant of a surface has to be taken into consideration as one of the important sources of information available to the observer about the spatial arrangements around him, that the slant can be given by a variety of cues, and that once the slant is given shapes are probably fairly well determined.

Ames, on the other hand, has demonstrated, particularly with the rotating trapezoid but also in a variety of other ways, that shape is a very important determinant of slant and that the slant thus determined is closely involved in the observer's distance judgments (Ames, Langden, Clark, et al.).

Little quantitative work exists, however, which specifically enables one to check the equivalent configurations derived earlier. In general, the evidence seems to fall within the limits of the invariance hypothesis (Eissler, Stavrianos, Thouless, for example), although there are strong suggestions of non-invariance under certain conditions (Stavrianos and Sheehan).

PERSPECTIVE

The consideration of size, shape, slant and distance inevitably leads us to perspective. As mentioned earlier, our considerations of perspective will be restricted to pointing out implications which follow from the preceding discussion and which are of interest to the student of perspective.

The upsurge of interest in perspective, starting with the 12th century and culminating in detailed geometric rules of perspective, is a fascinating phase of history. At least part of this interest can be attributed to the belief of the perspectivists that a clue to the representation of reality had been discovered. Objective, mathematical rules could, at last, be stated whereby external reality might be transposed to the canvas. An analogous enthusiasm attended the discovery of the stereoscope in the 19th century. Such search is foredoomed to failure since, as we have emphasized, reality exists for the individual in his own experience and not in a set of independent external characteristics. In the 16th century, Leonardo sounded a precautionary note of a different kind. He pointed out the ways in which he felt a perspective drawing, or indeed any painting, must necessarily differ from the actual view in terms of the visual cues available in the one situation that can not be duplicated in the other. We know today that some of the limitations Leonardo saw were technological in nature. With color stereoscopic photography, motion pictures, etc., it is possible to reproduce with sometimes startling fidelity the impingement aspects of a visual situation. Two facts, however, continue to limit all attempts to artificially reproduce apparent "reality." First, equivalent impingements cannot be produced in any simple way, and second, impingements alone do not determine the perceived reality, which is a unique, idiosyncratic experience into which a host of other factors enter. Nevertheless, artists and students of perspective continue occasionally to be bewildered by the fact that a proper application of the rules of perspective does not always produce the desired effect, or, conversely, that to produce the desired effect they must distort the rules. We shall briefly discuss some simple considerations which influence perspective as a depth cue.

The proper viewing distance

One of the goals of perspective drawing is for the observer to receive impingements which as closely as possible approximate those he would receive if he were viewing the scene itself. Every perspective drawing assumes a viewing distance, and the observer must view the drawing from this distance. Viewing from any other distance alters the perspective relationships in a predictable way. Detailed analyses have been carried out by Fry, Bartley and Linksz, among others.

The role of assumptions in perspective

Even if the principles of perspective are followed meticulously and the resulting picture is viewed from the proper distance, one cannot assume that an unequivocal and correct perception of distances, shapes, etc., will result. We do not have a one-way road starting with the perspective and ending with the apparent depth. The principle of equivalent configurations cannot be avoided. There are an infinite family of configurations all of which give the same perspective. We can illustrate this by pointing out that a trapezoid is a familiar example of a perspective drawing of a rectangle; or that a rectangle can also be a perspective drawing of a trapezoid. Assumptions as to shape can affect the ways in which the same perspective drawing is experienced.

This point was clear to Helmholtz when he wrote, "In many instances it is sufficient to know or assume that the object perceived has a certain regular form, in order to get a correct idea of its material shape from its perspective image as presented to us either by the eye or in an artificial drawing. If the objects portrayed are man's handiwork, such as a house or a table, we may presume that the angles are right angles, and the surfaces are flat or cylindrical or spherical. That is enough to obtain correct apperceptions of the object from an accurate perspective drawing. There is no difficulty about comprehending a perspective representation of a building or a piece of machinery, even when the details are fairly complicated. If the shading is good, it is easier still. But the most perfect drawing or even a photograph of a thing like a meteoric stone, a lump of ice, an anatomical preparation, or some other irregular object of this sort hardly affords any picture at all of the material form of the body."

Anomalies of perspective

We can generalize two sources of anomalous perspective, of which the preceding examples represent special cases.

1. *Shape of impingement constant but size varying.* Viewing a drawing from an inappropriate distance represents a special case. The general principle is clear from the earlier discussion of shape-equivalent configurations. With each change in size, a new family of equivalent configurations is introduced. The anomalous size may be deliberately introduced into a drawing for a particular effect. An example is Japanese perspective, in which the convergence of objectively parallel lines is much less than in conventional perspective. This produces an apparent divergence of parallel lines and greatly enhances the apparent size of distant objects (cf. Fry, Bartley).

A more common source of anomalous size of perspective impingements is through optical magnification. Donders early pointed this out, while Ames' telescope and cube demonstration was designed to illustrate these effects in general, and specifically to relate them to Japanese perspective.

A familiar example of the same effect is produced by telescopic lenses either on camera or television. Relative distances are greatly foreshortened with an attendant looming up of distant objects.

2. *Impingement constant but anomalous slant or relative distance given by other cues.* The example given before in which assumed shape differs from actual shape represents a special case.

The more general one is that in which other cues provide slant or relative distance indications which differ from those which would otherwise be provided by the perspective. If these other cues predominate, one perceives one of the equivalent configurations.

This case has not been systematically studied although it is frequently mentioned and examples cited. Donders described the possibility geometrically. That we do not experience anomalous perspective more often he attributed to the fact that other cues are commonly consistent with perspective rather than in conflict with it. Fry has described mathematically the case in which relative depth from stereopsis may be different from that provided by perspective. Aniseikonic glasses offer cases in which stereoscopic cues are deliberately distorted to differ from perspective and other cues.

The most striking examples are presented by continuously changing perspective. If an object is viewed while it is being rotated about an axis passing through the object, it will present impingements of constantly changing perspective shapes. However, at any given moment there is within the family of equivalent configurations, defined by the perspective at that moment, a member whose shape and slant correspond to that of the external object at the same moment. It is therefore possible to see, and one typically does see, an object of constant shape continuously changing its slant, i.e., rotating about an axis.

It may be, however, that at some given moment one does not perceive the equivalent configuration which corresponds to the actual object, but some other one. If this is so, then at the next succeeding moment there may not be a member which matches that just previously seen. The closest approximation may still differ markedly from it in shape, size, slant, or a combination of these. Hence, instead of an object of constant size and shape smoothly rotating, one typically perceives an object of changing size and shape moving at varying speeds and directions.

The rotating trapezoid of Ames is a well-known example. Striking effects can also be obtained by constructing a wire cube with a handle extending obliquely from one of the corners, gazing at the cube monocularly until the perspective has reversed, and then slowly rotating the cube. In his studies of the kinetic depth effect, Wallach has shown that one can learn to perceive the *appropriate* figure when presented with complex moving patterns that are initially meaningless. "Appropriate" refers to that figure which is common to all the families of equivalent configurations defined by the total set of impinging patterns. When this figure is perceived, the formerly anomalous, changing, or even non-existent depth effect is transferred into the consistent appearance of that figure smoothly rotating about its axis.

False perspective

Perhaps it is only fair at the conclusion of a discussion of anomalous perspective to point out once again that perspective is one of the most important of the depth cues, combining and compounding as it does both size and shape. Well-constructed false perspective produces an extremely convincing appearance of depth. In Ames' distorted rooms and "architect's" rooms the perspective shape is universally experienced rather than the actual shape. The principle has important architectural implications, and can be used to influence the apparent size and shape of a structure as well as the apparent size of people within it.

VI

Movement Parallax, Overlay, Togetherness Cues

In our survey of the individual depth cues we now turn to movement parallax, overlay, and the togetherness cues (coincidence of edge, sharpness of edge and detail, and double images). These cues to a certain extent form a consistent group in that they serve to provide indications as to whether or not one object is the same distance from the observer as another. They also provide quantitative indications of relative distances or absolute distances, but rarely does this function of the cues receive full credit.

The term "movement parallax" is usually used to refer to the apparent relative movements of objects as we move about among them. If one looks at a near object and moves his head left and right, the near object and some fixed point beyond it seem to move, relative to each other, in opposite directions, while two points at the same distance do not move relative to each other. Movement parallax is primarily a cue as to whether or not two objects are together in space, but, as we shall see, it can also serve as a cue to absolute distance and relative distance.

Overlay, sometimes called superposition, interposition, or masking, refers to the fact that near objects obscure parts of objects behind them. It provides a cue only as to whether one object is nearer or farther than another. The togetherness cues, conversely, provide indications as to whether or not one object is at the same distance as another. Coincidence of edge provides a cue that an object is the same distance as one with whose edge it lines up, but not the contrary, i.e., even if edges do not line up the two objects may be at the same distance. Sharpness of edge due to accommodation provides a cue that one object is, or is not, at the

same distance as another. It possibly provides a cue to relative
distances in terms of the magnitude of blurring and to farther or
nearer in terms of the particular characteristics of the blur. Sharpness of detail provides a cue that an object is farther than another
and also possibly a cue to relative distances in terms of the magnitude of the loss of detail. Double images provide our first binocular
cue. They may provide an indication that two objects are not at the
same distance and possibly a cue to relative distances in terms of the
magnitude of separation, and nearer or farther in terms of crossed or
uncrossed. These points will be discussed in more detail with respect
to each of the cues.

MOVEMENT PARALLAX

In the preceding chapter we assumed an absolutely motionless
observer viewing a perfectly static world except for a few very
restricted cases of apparent movement. Such a condition is, to say
the least, highly artificial and is rarely, if ever, encountered in concrete experience. Much more commonly, a moving observer views
a world which itself is in constant motion and change. The movement of objects relative to each other and relative to the observer
provides a most important visual space cue, movement parallax.

The recognition of movement parallax as a distance cue came
rather late in history. Whether this is because the principle was
unknown or considered too obvious to mention, we can only speculate. In any event, Wheatstone explicitly refers to movement parallax, although a later statement by Helmholtz is better known. It
reads as follows:

"In walking along, the objects that are at rest by the wayside
stay behind us; that is, they appear to glide past us in our field of
view in the opposite direction to that in which we are advancing.
More distant objects do the same way, only more slowly, while
very remote bodies like the stars maintain their permanent positions
in the field of view, provided the direction of the head and body
keep in the same directions. Evidently, under these circumstances,
the apparent angular velocities of objects in the field of view will
be inversely proportional to their real distances away; and, consequently, safe conclusions can be drawn as to the real distance of
the body from its apparent angular velocity.

"Moreover, in this case there is a relative displacement of objects at different distances with respect to each other. Those that are farther off as compared with those that are nearer seem to be advancing with the observer, whereas those that are nearer seem to be coming toward him; and the result is we have a very distinct apperception of the fact that they are unequally far from us. Suppose, for instance, that a person is standing still in a thick woods, where it is impossible for him to distinguish, except vaguely and roughly, in the mass of foliage and branches all around him what belongs to one tree and what to another, or how far apart the separate trees are, etc. But the moment he begins to move forward, everything disentangles itself, and immediately he gets an appreciation of the material contents of the woods and their relations to each other in space."

The general principle once stated is certainly sufficiently clear and obvious; anyone who wishes can easily convince himself of its validity by performing a simple modification of Helmholtz's demonstration. If one looks, with one eye closed, up into the dense foliage of a tree, the jumbled and disorderly array of leaves and branches, seen with head motionless, quickly assumes order and spatial localization if the head is moved continuously left and right six or eight inches.

Tschermak has given a rule which nicely describes what one, in general, experiences under conditions of movement parallax. "Near objects are apparently retarded or with respect to the principal object of attention located at a mean position move to the side opposite that of the observer. The object of attention seems to be at rest, farther objects seem to participate in the motion unless it occurs with excessive velocity. Finally, in distance fixation, far objects seem to be at rest, less far objects somewhat retarded, and near objects greatly retarded." However, simple though the bare facts of movement parallax may seem, its careful study leads us into some complexity.

Parallax-equivalent configurations

The first important point to note is that, in common with the cues discussed in the previous chapter, any particular case of movement parallax defines a family of equivalent configurations.

Since the configurations, in the case of movement parallax, include such aspects as the movement of the observer, equivalent "conditions" might be a better expression. For the sake of simplicity, however, the earlier term will be continued. Keeping the relevant impingement characteristics constant, there is a family of physical configurations all of which will provide the same impingement. The first step in the proof of this lies in determining what, in fact, is the relevant characteristic of the impingement. Graham has suggested that the impingement characteristic of the parallax cue can be expressed in terms of a relative angular velocity. He has derived expressions for this relative angular velocity for two cases (a) moving objects and a stationary observer and (b) stationary objects and a moving observer. This restriction is not necessary, however, and the following derivation, following Graham closely, provides an expression for the general case in which both observer and objects are moving. Graham's special cases may be deduced from this.

Referring to Figure VI-1, and assuming D to be very much

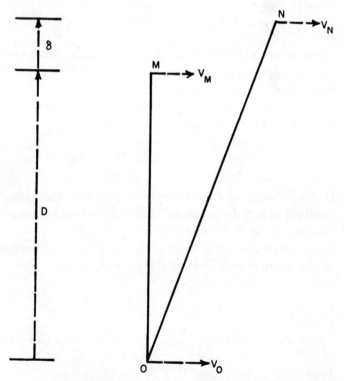

Figure VI-1   General case of movement parallax with an observer and two points all moving at different velocities.

greater than all other dimensions, the angular velocity of point M, relative to O, is given approximately by

$$\omega_M = \frac{V_M - V_O}{D} .$$ VI–1

Similarly,

$$\omega_N = \frac{V_N - V_O}{D + \delta} .$$ VI–2

The differential angular velocity, which provides the parallax cue, is

$$\omega = \omega_M - \omega_N = \frac{V_M - V_O}{D} - \frac{V_N - V_O}{D + \delta} .$$ VI–3

Simplifying,

$$\omega = \frac{\delta}{D^2} (V_M - V_O) + \frac{1}{D} (V_M - V_N) .$$ VI–4

It is immediately clear from Equation VI-4 that any specific case of movement parallax, i.e., ω = constant, defines a family of equivalent configurations.

Let us consider, for example, the case of stationary objects and a moving observer. Equation VI-4 reduces to

$$\omega = \frac{\delta V_O}{D^2}.$$ VI–5

If the velocity of the observer is constant, the criterion that ω be constant is met by a family of objects whose spacing increases with the square of their distance from the observer.

Another case of interest is that in which both objects are moving at the same speed. Equation VI-4 reduces to

$$\omega = \frac{\delta}{D^2} (V_M - V_O) .$$

The same parallax cue, i.e., ω = constant, is provided by a family of objects whose spacing varies inversely with the difference between their speed and that of the observer.

It should be noted that the assumption (made by Graham and

implicitly followed here) that the essential impingement characteristic related to the parallax cue is a relative angular velocity between two objects imposes an unnecessary restriction. Actually the basic parallax equation is given by equation VI-1.

$$\omega_M = \frac{V_M - V_O}{D}.$$

The angular velocity of a single object relative to the observer is inversely proportional to its distance, provided object and observer move at constant speed.

Parallax assumptions

As in our previous discussion of assumptions, we will assume that the invariance hypothesis holds. In the case of parallax this means that we substitute apparent distance, apparent separation and apparent velocities for the physical quantities in the above equations.

The basic assumption involved in movement parallax seems to be that of a "correction factor" which, for a single object, relates the apparent velocity of its movement, the apparent velocity of movement of the observer and the apparent distance of the object. Expressed symbolically, this is represented by the equation

$$\omega = \frac{\text{apparent } V_M - \text{apparent } V_O}{\text{apparent } D}.$$

The parallax invariance hypothesis ultimately reduces to the statement that the observer always introduces the proper correction factor in this form. "Proper," here, does not necessarily mean that the apparent quantities in the equation correspond to the physical quantities, but rather the apparent quantities properly satisfy the equation. A test of non-invariance would involve proof of the contrary. It should be noted that the assumed parallax correction factor refers to the case of a single object and not to relative movement between objects.

In addition to this basic correction factor there are other relevant assumptions. For purposes of simplification in the following discussion, we assume the apparent velocity of the observer is always correctly given and will not explicitly refer to it again. That is, we assume that the observer always correctly experiences his own velocity relative to some stable reference system. The fact that this assumption is usually valid presents one of the minor miracles, and major unsolved problems, of space perception. In order for a person's apparent velocity to equal his actual velocity, he must perform a tremendously complex calculation involving kinesthetic and vestibular cues of gross body movements, head movements, eye movements, and passive movement of the entire body as well as auditory, visual and tactual movement indications.

Parallax as a cue to absolute distance. In Equation VI-1, assuming the velocity of the object determines its distance.

Parallax as a cue to relative distance. In the case of two objects, assuming the velocities of the two objects determines the relationship between their relative distances and their absolute distance.

Note on apparent movement due to parallax

An important fact follows from the equation

$$\omega = \frac{V_M - V_O}{D},$$

assuming that the invariance hypothesis holds, i.e., that this equation is consistently satisfied perceptually. Consider a moving observer viewing a stationary object. If he correctly experiences his own velocity and sees the object at its correct distance, then he will see the object as actually stationary. However, if the apparent distance is not the same as the actual distance, then the solution of the equation calls for some velocity of the object. Hence the observer will experience the actually stationary object as apparently moving.

In general, referring to the other equations, if the apparent distance is not equal to the actual distance, then the objects will have movements attributed to them which are different from their actual movements.

EMPIRICAL FACTS OF PARALLAX

Very little controlled experimentation has been done with respect to movement parallax. What evidence there is, is entirely consistent with the preceding discussion, but considerably more experimentation is needed before we can make statements about parallax with any degree of experimental support. The following facts, however, may be considered to be established.

1. Observer monocularly viewing a single object in an otherwise dark room

a. *Observer moving, object stationary.* If the object is correctly localized, i.e., apparent distance equals physical distance, the object will appear stationary.

If the object is incorrectly localized, it appears to move.

These conclusions are based on unpublished experiments by the author, using playing cards of various sizes, monocularly viewed, to produce incorrect localization.

b. *Object moving, observer stationary.* If the object is correctly localized, its apparent velocity is the same as its physical velocity.

If the object is incorrectly localized, its apparent velocity is different from its physical velocity. If apparent distance is less than physical distance, apparent velocity is less than physical velocity and conversely.

2. Moving observer viewing two or more stationary objects

If the objects are correctly localized on the basis of other cues prior to movement, the addition of parallax provides additional supporting information but does not appreciably alter the perceived situation. This is the case of common observation.

The case in which the objects are incorrectly localized prior to movement has also been studied experimentally. We are here, properly speaking, dealing with a case of cue-conflict of the sort discussed in Chapter IX. Two different results have been reported.

a. The parallax serves as a cue to relative distance and the objects change in apparent localization to approximately their actual positions (Bourdon, Helmholtz, Wheatstone, Ames). This represents the only case usually referred to in texts. It is the case of common observation if other cues are absent or minimal (cf. earlier quotation from Helmholtz).

b. The parallax does not overcome the other cues which are giving an incorrect apparent localization to the object. In this event parallax is seen as apparent relative movement of the objects, which remain at their previous incorrect apparent distances.

Apparent movement thus introduced by parallax is not dependent on any actual relative movement. If two stationary objects are
physically at the same distance, $\omega = O$ in equation VI-5, i.e., there
is no relative movement between them. However, if the objects are
seen at different apparent distances due to other cues, the introduction of head movement makes the objects appear to move relative to each other.

These effects have never been systematically studied, but these
conclusions are based on unpublished experiments by Ames and
the author. In these experiments the Ames watch-card-magazine
demonstration, aniseikonic glasses, and distorted rooms (as described by Ittelson) were used as well as the conventional stereoscope and the pseudoscope. All of these cases provide objects at
apparent distances other than their actual distances, and the effect
of introducing parallax can be observed.

3. Parallax thresholds

These have been measured for the case of three rods (Tschermak) and two rods (Graham, Zegers).

OVERLAY

Overlay as a depth cue refers to the fact that a near object may
obscure part of a far object. The discovery of overlay lies in the
early history of pictorial art. It is one of the most important and
most common depth cues available to the artist, and examples of
its use can be found in the oldest existing drawings. Indeed, it is
next to impossible to draw anything except perhaps some geometrical designs and abstract shapes without making use of overlay.

In spite of, or perhaps because of, its obviousness, overlay does
not seem to have been specifically referred to and described as a
depth cue until Helmholtz discussed it in a famous passage. "For
instance, when two hills are visible far away, the base of one extending in front of the other partly concealing it, we conclude immediately that the hill that is hidden is the more remote of the two; for
if this were not the case, one of the objects would be different from
that of any other hill that ever was seen, not to mention the strange
coincidence that the outline of this peculiar hill should happen to
be exactly contingent by the contour of the other one. It might be
a possible explanation of the picture presented to the eye but it

certainly would be contrary to all experience. Of course, the same sort of thing can occur with all kinds of objects when some of them are partially concealed by the others. Even if we are thoroughly unacquainted with their forms, the mere fact that the contour line of the covering object does not change its direction where it joins the contour of the one behind it, will generally enable us to decide which is which."

Actually the question of overlay as a depth cue is broader than suggested by Helmholtz, and includes the fact that an object not only obscures parts of other objects beyond it, but also obscures part of the background. The general phenomenon has been studied as *figure and ground.* The pioneer work of Rubin in the field has been well summarized by Woodworth and Schlosberg.

"Rubin found it possible to see any well-marked part of a visual field as the figure, leaving the rest as the ground. If the total field consists of a black portion and a white portion meeting in a contour, either the black or the white portion can be seen as figure, the other being the ground. If either the black or the white portion is entirely enclosed by the other, the enclosed portion is more easily seen as the figure, but with practice the enclosing portion can be so seen. If the contour separating the two portions is approximately vertical without enclosing either part of the field, figure and ground are easily reversed. When the reversal occurs, the change of appearance is surprising because the shape of the two parts of the field is very different—which is rather curious since these shapes depend on the common contour separating the two parts.

"The phenomenal differences between figure and ground are classified by Rubin as follows: (1) the figure has form, while the ground is relatively formless, or if the ground has form it is due to some other figuration upon it and not to the contour separating it from the figure; (2) the ground seems to extend continuously behind the figure and not to be interrupted by the figure; (3) thus the figure has some of the character of a *thing*, whereas the ground appears like unformed *material;* (4) the figure tends to appear in front, the ground behind; (5) the figure is more impressive, better remembered, and more apt to suggest meaning."

The concept of figure-ground relations is certainly a much larger one than is overlay as a depth cue, carrying as it does widespread philosophical and practical implications. It seems clear, however, that *in so far as it functions as a depth cue* the figure-ground relationship belongs in the same category as overlay of one object on another object. We shall include the fact that an object obscures part of the background behind it in our discussion of overlay.

Overlay-equivalent configurations

It is readily shown diagrammatically that any given example of overlay defines an infinite family of equivalent configurations.

The generalization of this fairly obvious geometrical fact into a mathematical expression will not be attempted. We can draw general conclusions about the nature of the equivalent configurations, however, even in the absence of such an expression. It seems clear that, although any given impingement defines an infinite family of equivalent configurations, these actually reduce to two sub-groups. In one group the common contour between the two objects forms the boundary of one of the objects (the near one), in the other group it forms the boundary of the other object (the far one). (There remains, of course, the special case in which it forms the boundary of both objects, which will be discussed in the section on coincidence of edge.)

Note on the importance of the common contour

The difficulty of going beyond the above qualitative description and arriving at a mathematically exact statement of overlay-equivalent configurations stems in part from the difficulty in specifying the relevant characteristics of the impingement. The most general specification would include all the information necessary for identifying each of the two objects. Nevertheless, it is clear that in this process what we have referred to as the common contour between the two objects plays an especially important role.

A rigid definition of this common contour has been provided by Ratoosh: "Consider a projection of figures onto a plane perpendicular to the visual axis, such that the nodal point of the eye is the point of projection. In such a perspective transformation all objects will be represented by simple closed curves. (Without any loss in generality only two figures will be treated here. The same reasoning may be extended to apply to any number of objects.) A necessary condition for interposition (overlay) to become effective as a cue is that the curves of the two objects in the plane of projection have a common boundary. A point at which the boundaries of the curves meet will be called a point of intersection. Clearly there will be two points of intersection for a common boundary."

The characteristics of this common boundary play two important roles in overlay.

1. *Identification of figures.* The shape of the common boundary may enable the observer to identify one or both of the figures, thus determining which overlays which. This is most marked in some figure-ground examples.

2. *Continuity of contour at points of intersection.* In this regard, Ratoosh has written, "Continuity of the first derivative of the object's contour at the points of intersection is the sole determiner of relative distance." This contribution of Ratoosh may be worth while in that it provides a rigid definition of what is meant by continuity of contour at the points of intersection as an impingement characteristic related to overlay. But Ratoosh errs when he says that this and this alone is *the* impingement characteristic related to overlay as a cue. The reasons for refuting this claim are: First, figure-ground effects do not depend on any points of intersection. The figure may be continuously surrounded by the ground. A book on the desk or the picture on the wall certainly provide overlay cues but there are no points of intersection between the contours of the desk and those of the book, or the wall and the picture. Second, if the two objects are identified by other information, what happens at the points of intersection may become irrelevant.

We are left with the conclusion that the role of the characteristics of the common boundary at the points of intersection is approximately as follows: The contour which continues past the point of intersection in the expected direction will be seen as belonging to the covering object. In the case of entirely unfamiliar objects with otherwise continuous boundaries, continuity at the point of intersection will be expected.

Overlay assumptions

The only relevant assumption is that of the shape and wholeness of the objects. This assumption determines to which object the common boundary belongs, and it is this object which is perceived in front.

If the objects are familiar, the assumption of the shape and wholeness of the objects is easily arrived at. If the objects, however, are completely unfamiliar or abstract, then the characteristics of the common boundary and the points of intersection will probably be important in arriving at this assumption. It is probable that in addition to an assumption of wholeness of the objects, we are also dealing here with an assumption as to the continuity of the boundaries of the objects.

Empirical facts of overlay

In general, overlay follows the invariance hypothesis in the sense that one of the two sub-groups described under equivalent configurations is seen. The obscured object is seen behind the obscuring (Helmholtz, Ames, Ratoosh, Rubin, Chapanis).

In the absence of other indications an object tends to appear at the same distance as the background which it overlays (Ames, Gibson, Rubin).

Conflicting overlay indications result in either an anomalous situation or alternation between two possible perceptions (Ratoosh, Rubin).

Overlay has been studied in conflict with binocular stereopsis (Schriever) and size (Ames). Overlay is usually found to be the dominant cue; in cases in which it is not dominant, the phenomenon of *apparent transparency* has been reported, that is, the overlaying object is seen through an apparently transparent object.

THE TOGETHERNESS CUES

1.   Coincidence of edge

Coincidence of edge is, properly speaking, a special case of overlay in which the common boundary belongs to both objects which are seen at the same distance. Like overlay, this cue has long been used by pictorial artists. It is also a cue which may cause pictorial artists difficulty: since two adjacent figures on a canvas necessarily have a common boundary, this always acts as a cue toward seeing them at the same distance which, however, may not be the artist's intention.

Once again we have an example here of a cue which has long been utilized by artists but which waited until very recently to be intellectualized and specifically described and experimented with, the first explicit recognition of coincidence of edge as a distance cue being by Ames. The equivalent configurations for any particular case of coincidence of edge will be analogous to those described in the case of overlay. The critical difference lies in the assumption that the common boundary belongs to *both* of the objects. If the boundary is assigned to both the objects they will be seen at the same distance. This statement has been experimentally proved by Ames who has studied coincidence of edge as an isolated indication and in conflict with size.

2. Sharpness of edge due to accommodation

Accommodation has usually been treated as a kinesthetic rather than a visual cue. That is, the depth cue provided by accommodation is usually considered to be via the muscular effort of accommodation rather than through any effect in the retinal excitation. However, there is a way in which accommodation might function as a visual rather than a kinesthetic cue. When the eye is accommodated for an object at a particular distance, the impingements from that object are most clearly focused on the retina. Objects at any other distances are less sharply focused. Therefore, we have the possible cue that all sharply focused objects are at the same distance. Similarly, blurred objects would be at different distances than sharply focused objects, the greater the blurring the greater the distance difference. Furthermore, objects closer than the accommodation distance have slightly different blur characteristics than objects at greater distances. All of this adds up to the fact that accommodation offers the possibility of providing quantitative indications of relative distance.

There is a growing tendency among writers on visual perception to assume that this is in fact the way accommodation functions as a distance cue, in sharp contrast to the earlier emphasis on the kinesthetic cue. However, there is actually no direct experimental evidence, and in this book accommodation, together with convergence, will be treated as non-visual cues in Chapter VIII. This more traditional approach to the subject is followed simply because of the complete inability, in the usual accommodation experiment, to·distinguish between kinesthetic cues and the possible visual effects. Actually, as we shall see, the relation between accommodation and apparent distance is much more complex than the preceding discussion would indicate. It is included at this point because in so far as it serves as a distance cue, accommodation most probably operates through the differential blurring of images.

3. Sharpness of detail due to distance (aerial perspective)

It is a common observation that, if we look at a distant landscape, objects lose their sharpness of detail as they recede from us, and also change color in definite ways. This general fact is referred to as aerial perspective and is usually attributed to the presence of droplets of moisture and particles of dust in the air between us and the distant objects. The specific effects are loss of detail, decrease in saturation and brightness of colors, and a shift of hue toward the bluish-purple. Aerial perspective is usually listed among the visual distance cues. However, aside from its use by artists, and its consistency with everyday observation, there seems to be no direct experimental evidence. There is no doubt, however, that aerial perspective does function as a distance cue approximately as indicated above, i.e., objects of about the same sharpness of detail and color characteristics are seen at the same distance, while less detailed, less color saturated, etc., objects are seen farther away.

4. Double images

In the case of double images, we have another example of a depth cue which is logically indicated but for which there is little or no experimental evidence. When both eyes are fixated on a point at a given distance, that point is seen as a single image, as are all other points lying on the horopter (so-defined). All points lying nearer or farther are seen as double. Furthermore, the greater the distance from the single vision horopter, the greater the distance between two images; while objects lying nearer than the horopter are "crossed" (the right eye image is seen to the left) those lying further than it are "un-crossed." Double images offer the possibility of providing quantitative indications of relative distance. As in the case of accommodation, there is a growing tendency to attribute depth effects due to convergence to this visual factor rather than to the kinesthetic cues. Again, however, there is no direct evidence that double images actually do function as distance cues, although most probably they do.

ILLUMINATION, BRIGHTNESS AND SHADING

These three cues fall into a somewhat indeterminate category and will be briefly discussed although there is very little experimental evidence on which to base conclusions. There can not be any doubt that the lighting and coloring of objects and surfaces are related to their apparent spatial properties. The exact nature of this relationship remains obscure. These cues are, however, among the most important ones available to the artist, and their skillful and original use presents a continuing challenge.

Illumination

Let us consider a surface of area A, normal to the line of sight, at a distance D, sufficiently great so that the solid angle β subtended by A at the point of observation O is given approximately by $\frac{A}{D^2}$. The surface A is reflecting (or emitting) light uniformly in all directions. Let i be the brightness, or intensity of reflected light per unit area, and $I = iA$ be the total intensity of light reflected by A, in the direction of the observer.

The intensity of light reaching the observer per unit area of the source decreases proportionally to the square of the distance of the source from the observer. The total intensity of light at the point of observation, I_o, is given by multiplying the received intensity per unit area of the source by the area of the source, hence,

$$I_o = c\frac{iA}{D^2} = c\frac{I}{D^2} . \qquad \text{VI-6}$$

If i_o is the intensity per unit angle at the point of observation, then

$$I_o = \beta i_o.$$

Substituting

$$\beta = \frac{A}{D^2}$$

$$I_o = \frac{i_o A}{D^2} .$$

Therefore, substituting in Equation VI-6

$$I_o = \frac{i_o A}{D^2} = c\frac{iA}{D^2}$$

$$i_o = ci. \hspace{3cm} \text{VI–7}$$

Equation VI-7 states that the brightness, or intensity of light per unit angle, at the point of observation is dependent only on the brightness of the observed object. This means that the family of equivalent configurations defined by a given impinging brightness, expressed by i_o = constant, consists of any and all surfaces of a given brightness i. Conversely, the impinging brightness of an object is independent of the distance of that object from the observer.

Equation VI-6 provides a more serious limitation. For a given total intensity of illumination impinging on the point of observation, the expression

$$\frac{iA}{D^2} = \text{constant}$$

defines the family of equivalent configurations. For a constant brightness, i, the surface must decrease in size as the distance decreases in such a way as to maintain a constant visual angle. Or, considering a constant-size object, its brightness must vary with the square of the distance.

Exactly how, or even if, illumination functions as a distance cue is not clear. The above discussion would indicate that in all probability the depth effect does not depend on brightness or energy per unit area but on the total impinging light energy. In any event, this is the only aspect which has a consistent and demonstrable relationship to distance. The experimental evidence, though slight, is at least consistent with this possibility. If two objects of similar size and distance are viewed monocularly in a dark room, the brighter appears closer (Duncan, Ames, Munster). Similarly if the intensity of a single object is continuously varied, the object appears to approach and recede (Ames). If the intensity of the general illumination of a room or any enclosed space is varied, the space seems to expand or contract, as can be attested to by anyone who has felt a theater close in on him as the lights dim. This general effect is probably related to gamma movement, which refers to the fact that when an object is suddenly illuminated, it appears to expand.

Color

A principle adhered to by artists is that warm, saturated, bright colors approach while cold, unsaturated, dark colors recede. This is simply a recognition of the facts of aerial perspective: with increasing distance, objects tend not only to lose detail but, in color, to go toward the unsaturated blues. Whether or not this cue operates at other than extreme distances is not clear. There certainly does not seem to be any other demonstrably consistent relation between color and distance.

Experimental evidence is very slight, but in general tends to be confirmatory. Using the task of setting discs of red, blue, green, and grey seen against a black background to appear equidistant monocularly, Leventhal concluded that "red is perceived closest, green somewhat farther away, and blue still farther in relation to grey." Using a similar task, Johns and Sumner obtained similar results with yellow and white appearing relatively near, and green, blue and black relatively farther away when compared to neutral grey. Other less well-controlled studies report similar results.

An important unpublished experiment by W. M. Smith, however, suggests an alternative interpretation of these results. Using a modification of Ames' Thereness-Thatness apparatus, he had his subjects set a single rectangle of color viewed monocularly to appear the same distance as a fixed point on a well-structured binocular reference alley. For his test colors he used patches from a Munsell color chart varying along the three dimensions of hue, saturation and brightness. These patches were viewed against a uniform yellowish-grey background. The results indicated large and significant differences between settings for various patches which, however, were not in accord with the usual hypothesis. However, an analysis of the data along the three dimensions showed that those samples closest, along *any* particular dimension, to the background were seen farthest away while the samples less like the background were seen nearer. Or, to generalize, the more a color (either in hue, saturation, brightness or a combination) approximated the background, the more it appeared to recede towards the background. The more a color differed from the background, the farther it stood out from the background. Smith emphasizes that his conclusion is tentative and needs further experimental verification. Its importance lies in offering a different interpretation which is still consistent with all the other existing evidence.

Shading

Light and shadows are used by the artist to convey an impression not of distance, but of solidity. Indeed, shading is perhaps the most important tool the artist has for conveying the three-dimensional character of objects and it is probably an equally important everyday cue as well.

Experiments have shown that completely uniform, shadowless illumination can convert three-dimensional objects into apparently two-dimensional ones, while changing the illumination can change their appearance. In addition to their three-dimensional effect, light and shadows also offer cues to relative distance. Unpublished observations by the author show that if a particular pattern of light and shadow is localized by other cues, then objects which apparently partake of this particular pattern will be seen at the same distance. Similarly, an object will be seen in front of another on which it apparently casts a shadow. Controlled experiments in this area are almost completely lacking.

Concluding note on illumination, color and shading

It seems intuitively obvious, and consistant with the evidence, that illumination, color, and shading do serve as cues to apparent depth. However, the exact manner in which they function seems to be qualitatively different from all the other cues. In all other cases, there is some impingment characteristic which, for a given object, varies in some predictable way with the distance of the object. Not so, except in some relatively trivial or special cases, with illumination, color, and shading. It seems most reasonable to consider these cues as contributing to the integration of a complex situation. The observer organizes the total experience in such a way as to make the best "sense" out of it, that is, to make it correspond to the most highly probably condition. Illumination, color and shading play a crucial role in this overall integration.

VII

Binocular Stereopsis

HISTORICAL INTRODUCTION

All organisms that have eyes have two eyes, symmetrically located on the right and left sides of the body. In most lower organisms these two eyes view different regions in space on the right and left, respectively. In man and certain other higher organisms, however, the two fields of view of the eyes very largely overlap and cover a single region in space more or less directly ahead of the organism. This makes possible the viewing of this region in space with either eye separately or with both eyes simultaneously. The two eyes viewing the same region in space from two different points present in experience a single view of the external world.

This strange fact of two eyes seeing as one has apparently always been of interest to man, as is testified for instance by the myths of the Cyclops. The ancient Greeks were certainly aware of the problem of binocular vision. Euclid is at pains to demonstrate that when a sphere whose diameter is less than the distance between the eyes is viewed with both eyes, more than half a sphere is visible, while if the diameter of the sphere is greater than the distance between the eyes, less than half the sphere is visible. Euclid's interesting example is found recurring in all early writers on this subject. Thus, they had available the evidence to show that the single view of the world obtained with two eyes is formed from two dissimilar views in each eye.

While Euclid was primarily interested in the geometrical problem presented by two eyes, Galen, the famous physician of the second century, was concerned with the application of this geometrical construction to the problems of binocular vision. In his great work *On the use of the parts of the human body*, he provides diagrams illustrating Euclid's proposition and then, for those not mathematically inclined, he adds: "But if any person does not understand these demonstrations by means of lines, he will finally give his assent to them when he has made the following experiment. Standing near a column and shutting each of the eyes in succession, when the right eye is shut, some of those parts of the column which were previously seen by the right eye on the right side of the column will not now be seen by the left eye, and when the left eye is shut, some of those parts which were formerly seen by the left eye on the left side of the column will not now be seen by the right eye. But when we, at the same time, open both eyes, both these will be seen, for a greater part is concealed when we look with either of the two eyes than when we look with both at the same time."

Porta, a student of optics in the sixteenth century, refers both to this passage from Galen and to the propositions of Euclid and is struck by the fact implicit in these two writers, but not explicitly stated by them, that the single binocular picture is formed by the union of two dissimilar pictures. Believing this to be impossible, Porta advanced the theory that we see with only one eye at a time, rapidly alternating between the two.

As may be expected, Leonardo da Vinci did not let this interesting fact escape from his observation. In his *Treatise on painting*, he refers to the difference between the pictures seen by each eye, and concludes that, "A painting, though conducted with the greatest art, and finished to the last perfection, both with regard to its contours, its lights, its shadows, and its colors, can never show a relief equal to that of the natural objects unless these be viewed at a distance and with a single eye." He demonstrated this by means of an illustration of a small sphere viewed with two eyes and showed that the sphere is transparent in the sense that it hides nothing behind it, while a sphere in painting necessarily cannot possess this property.

About a century after Leonardo, Aguilonius conducted the first major investigation of binocular vision which he published in 1613. He recognized that the two eyes see different views of an object, but, since he rejected Porta's view of vision by only one eye at a time, he was at a loss to explain why the two dissimilar views do

not result in a blurred and confused image when united in binocular
vision. In commenting on the different views obtained by the two
eyes, he says, "This, I think, is perfectly evident, but I consider it
as worthy of admiration how it happens that bodies seen by both
eyes are not all confused and shapeless though we view them by the
optical axes fixed on the bodies themselves." This leads him to the
obvious logical conclusion that, "Since the images in each eye are
dissimilar, the representation of the object must appear confused
and disturbed to the primary sense." But, he adds, "This view of
the subject is certainly consistent with reason, but what is truly
wonderful is that it is not correct, for bodies are seen clearly and
distinctly with both eyes when the optic axes are converged upon
them. The reason of this, I think, is that the bodies do not appear
to be single because the apparent images which are formed of each
of them in separate eyes exactly coalesce, but because the common
sense imparts its aid equally to each eye, exerting its own power
equally in the same manner as the eyes are converged by means of
their optical axes. Whatever body, therefore, each eye sees with
the eyes conjoined, the common sense makes a single notion, not
composed of the two which belong to each eye, but belonging and
accommodated to the imaginative faculty to which it, the common
sense, assigns it." It is interesting to note that when reason and
experience disagree, Aguilonius unhesitatingly accepted the evidence of experience. Truly, the era of modern science had begun.

In illustrating the thesis that the two eyes see different views of
an object, Aguilonius repeated the theorems of Euclid relative to
the viewing of a sphere, which he demonstrated by means of a diagram and then proceeded to extend this to cylinders, cones, and,
indeed, all objects.

Following Aguilonius, the fact that the two eyes receive different views of an object was recognized by most writers on optics.
Gassendi, forty-five years after Aguilonius, makes the observation
that we see the left side of the nose with our left eye, and the right
side of our nose with the right eye, thus providing two pictures
which are sufficiently dissimilar to convince the most confirmed
skeptic. Robert Smith, in his 1738 work, *A compleat system of optics*,
refers at length to Leonardo's discussion of binocular vision as
related to painting, and supplements this with a demonstration of
his own. He instructs one to place a long ruler "between the eye-

brows and extended directly forward, with its flat sides respecting the right hand and the left." Under which conditions, "the right side of the ruler seen by the right eye will appear on the right hand, and the left side on the left hand," which he demonstrates by means of a figure.

Harris, in 1775, published his *Treatise on opticks,* in which he noted that the fact that we can see around small objects is an important factor in determining relief. "By the parallax on account of the distance betwixt our eyes, we can distinguish, besides the front, part of the two sides of a near object not thicker than the said distance, and this gives a visible relieve to such objects which helps greatly to raise or detach them from the plane in which they lie. Thus the nose on a face is the more remarkably raised by our seeing both sides of it at once." Porterfield, in his 1759 *Treatise on the eye,* gives drawings of an object as seen by each eye in binocular vision.

This brief historical review shows that, by the start of the 19th century, a long line of illustrious writers on optics, dating back to the ancient Greeks, had noted and explicitly stated that the two eyes in binocular vision see different views of the same object. We might add that Descartes had likened the convergence of the two eyes on an object to the feeling out of space by a blind man using two staves. Yet, while all these writers had noted differences between the use of one eye and the use of two eyes, they all failed to specify exactly, and in an experimentally verifiable manner, in what way two eyes function differently from one. Our primary problem will be to pursue this question further—to determine in what way the factors introduced by the use of two eyes, that are not present when either eye is used singly, function in determining our perception of space.

Helmholtz, Hering and many others interested in this problem found that if vertical threads, viewed with the head in a fixed position, are arranged so as to appear to be in a frontal parallel plane, the threads will not, in the usual case, lie in a physical frontal parallel plane. The shape of the physical surface formed by the threads will vary with the distance of observation in the manner illustrated in Figure VII-1. The same effect may be obtained by setting points of light to appear in a straight line; when viewed from above, the line is found to have the physical shapes indicated in the diagram. Or, as Hardy has stated: "With more fun, equal interest, and less

Figure VII-I   The apparent fronto-parallel plane curves toward or away from the observer as a function of fixation distance.

bother, a similar experiment can be performed in broad daylight. With the subject squatting or lying so that the eyes are near ground level, an assistant arranges five golf balls on a relatively flat lawn or green 20 to 40 feet (6 to 12 meters) away. The balls are to be arranged so that they appear to lie in a perfectly straight line at right angles to the line of sight. At this distance, the physical curve will probably be convex toward the observer." This finding, that the binocularly visually straight is not physically straight, was extended by Hillebrand to include lines and planes apparently at right angles to those described above. This is the Hillebrand alley experiment, in which vertical wires or star points are arranged to appear in two straight and parallel rows, as the walls of an alley or hallway. When this is done, the physical arrangement of strings or star points is neither straight nor parallel, but of a characteristic curve which varies with such factors as distance from the observer, and from observer to observer. The type of curves obtained is shown in Figure VII-2.

The demonstrations that the binocularly apparently straight is not physically straight, and the apparently parallel is not physically

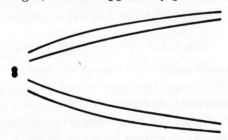

Figure VII-2   The apparent "straight and parallel" curves lie inside the apparent "equidistant" curves.

parallel are incontrovertible. This must be taken into account in any adequate theory of binocular vision. Further interesting observations along the same line were obtained from an extension of the Hillebrand alley experiment by Blumenfeld. He instructed his observers to set the two sides of the alley so that they appeared equidistant. When this had been done and recorded, he instructed the same observers to set the same test objects so that they would form two walls which appeared straight and parallel. Blumenfeld reported different curves obtained under these two different instructions, with the "equidistant" curve consistently outside the "straight and parallel" curve.

These results have been particularly fascinating to students of binocular vision because, in terms of Euclidean geometry, the two instructions, "straight and parallel" and "equidistant" are the same under the conditions of the experiment. Since different results are obtained under these two instructions, one is forced to conclude that at least in binocular vision, straight and parallel and equidistant are not the same. This demonstrates—what has long been known to mathematicians—that the Euclidean geometry which we all are taught almost at the beginning of our thinking life is not an inevitable law of nature but rather is a man-made construction which rests upon certain axioms. The geometry follows inevitably from these axioms, but whether or not the geometry represents any real situation depends upon the validity of the axioms. As Whitehead has said, "Euclid's geometry was once supposed to be an exact description of the external world. The only world of which it is an accurate description is the world of Euclidean geometry."

It is neither mathematically impossible nor contrary to everyday experience that there is geometry other than Euclidean. Indeed, we can expect to experience relationships in the visual perception of space which are not possible in Euclidean geometry.

THE DISCOVERY OF STEREOPSIS

We have already mentioned that at the start of the 19th century most writers were aware that the use of two eyes provides additional depth indications, and that each eye sees a different view of the same object. They were concerned with the paradox of a single clear image apparently resulting from two dissimilar images. Indeed, this paradox made Lord Bacon deny the superiority of binocular vision. He even found evidence to support his belief: "We see more exquisitely with one eye shut than with both, because the vital spirits thus unite themselves the more and become the stronger, for we may find by looking in a glass whilst we shut one eye that the pupil of the other dilates."

The first truly stereoscopic experiment had actually been reported by Robert Smith in 1738, but he failed to interpret it properly. It remained for Wheatstone, in 1838, to achieve the insight which could order the facts into a coherent whole. He recognized that the two different views of an object presented to the two eyes is not the problem but the explanation of binocular space perception. He showed that these different views may easily be determined from the well-known laws of perspective, and continued: "Yet they seem to have escaped the attention of every philosopher and artist who has treated the subject of vision and perspective. I can ascribe this inattention only to this circumstance, that the results being contrary to a principle that was very generally maintained by optical writers, viz., that objects can be seen single only when their images fall on corresponding points of the two retinae. If the consideration ever arose in their minds, it was hastily discarded, under the conviction that if the pictures presented to the two eyes are under certain circumstances dissimilar, the differences must be so small that they need not be taken into account." He then referred to Leonardo's comment on the apparent transparency of a small sphere, and noted that if Leonardo had used a cube instead of a sphere, he might have made this discovery. But "he failed to do this, and no subsequent writer within my knowledge has supplied the omission. That two obviously dissimilar pictures are projected on the two retinae when a single object is viewed while the optic axes converge must, therefore, be regarded as a new fact on the theory of vision."

In the light of the historical references previously made, it is evident that this statement is not literally true, for many writers had noted the dissimilar pictures projected on the two retinae. It is true in the sense that none of the writers had recognized the significance of this fact. Since no writer likes to be told that he has overlooked a simple and obvious fact, Wheatstone's discovery was greeted by some with loud cries that it had been known all along. This "we knew it all along" approach to new insight is beautifully exemplified in the book on the stereoscope by Brewster. He traced in detail the history which we have already given, and we are primarily indebted to him for it. He then asked: "What student of perspective is there, master or pupil, male or female, who does not know as certainly as he knows his alphabet, that the picture of a chair or table or anything else drawn from one point of sight, or as seen by one eye placed at that point, is necessarily dissimilar to another drawing of the same object taken from another point of sight or as seen by the other eye placed in a point two-and-one-half inches distant from the first? If such a person is to be found, we might then admit that dissimilarity of the pictures in each eye was not known to every student of perspective." Brewster concluded that "It is inconceivable on what ground he (Wheatstone) could imagine himself to be the discoverer of so palpable and notorious a fact as that the pictures of a body seen by two eyes, two points of sight, must be dissimilar." It is interesting to note, as a sideline to this controversy, that in 1831, seven years before Wheatstone's publication, Brewster himself had written a treatise on optics, in which no mention is made of this "palpable" fact, and further, throughout his book on the stereoscope, Brewster consistently misinterprets the principle of this instrument. He, the first great authority on the optics of the stereoscope, never understood the underlying perceptual theory. He firmly believed that the stereoscope operated on the basis of convergence (cf. Chapter VIII), and never understood Wheatstone's real discovery—that it is the mere fact of difference between the two images presented to the two eyes which in and of itself can arouse an impression of distance. Wheatstone not only recognized this fundamental fact of binocular vision, but invented an instrument to demonstrate it, which he named the stereoscope.

In addition, Wheatstone made a start in the direction of a theory of binocular vision, indicated by his statement that if instead of actual objects, perspective projections of the same objects are used, "The observer will perceive a figure of three dimensions, the exact counterpart of the object from which the drawings were made."

Wheatstone was a physicist of repute and his single excursion into matters psychological remains a model of lucid, comprehensive and systematic experimentation. The hundred or more years since Wheatstone wrote have seen basic experimental and theoretical additions and modifications to his contributions.

The 19th century, however, would not wait for the slow scientific resolution of the theoretical problems of binocular space perception. The plain facts of the stereoscope were too vivid, too obvious and too easily accessible to everyone. The parlor stereoscope became a symbol of the Victorian era. Its inventor, Oliver Wendell Holmes, carried away by the spirit of the times, wrote that one no longer needed to contemplate with dismay the eventual destruction of great architectural works since their solid corporeity could be preserved for all time on the slides of the stereoscope.

In retrospect, this popular enthusiasm fits readily into the historical context of mid-nineteenth century science. The facts of reality were firmly in hand, all that remained to be learned about the physical world were more figures beyond the decimal point. Maxwell's field equations were a quarter of a century away and Michelson-Morley's experiment still another two decades.

There was, however, a serious gap in this picture. Physics, which over the previous two centuries had painstakingly built up a complete picture of the nature of the "real" world, still had no way of accounting for man's ever becoming aware of this world. Contemporary psychophysiology was of little help in this dilemma. The same year that saw the publication of Wheatstone's first paper (1838) also witnessed the appearance of Müller's *Handbuch* in which the doctrine of the specific energy of nerves received its first important formulation. It is interesting to compare viewpoints. Müller offered not even the pattern of stimulation of the sense organs but rather a mysterious electro-chemical disturbance taking place at a nerve-ending hidden somewhere in the dark recesses of the brain. Wheatstone offered the real world of every-day experience in all its comforting three-dimensional solidity. Small wonder that the popular and scientific imagination was stirred by the latter appeal. A direct path was charted between the reality of contemporary physics and the experience of men.

FROM WHEATSTONE TO AMES

The general principle of stereoscopic vision was never precisely formulated by Wheatstone. He remained satisfied with a verbal statement backed by the solid evidence of the stereoscope. The investigators following him in the study of binocular space perception early recognized the need for a rigorous mathematical analysis.

Actually, however, the start of a mathematical study of binocular vision antedates Wheatstone, and was initially concerned with the problem of singleness of vision. By the time Wheatstone wrote, the Vieth-Müller circle had been established as the predicted shape of the horopter, on the basis of the assumption that corresponding points on the two retinae bear a fixed and equal relationship to their respective foveae and horizontal meridians. With the invention and study of the stereoscope, the problem of singleness of vision, and the horopter in general, was joined by that of stereopsis; the two have been approached along parallel paths since.

The geometric analysis of stereoscopic vision in the period between Wheatstone and Ames centered about two separate aspects of the geometry: (1) the direction of pointing of the eyes (convergence) and (2) the difference between the images formed on the retinae of the two eyes (disparity). These two aspects provided the background for the conflict between Brewster and Wheatstone. The former staked his all on convergence, which he rightly pointed out was not a new principle. The latter owes his importance in this field for having discovered and recognized the significance of disparity.

The neat, geometrical exactness of the triangulation involved in the pointing of the two eyes at a single object intrigued many. It was simple, easily understood, and, at least geometrically, entirely adequate. Only gradually did an equally rigorous analysis of disparity emerge, until with Helmholtz and Hering the definition of binocular disparity reached essentially the form in which it is used today. Ogle's definition provides an excellent recent example: "Stereoscopic perception of the difference in depth between the point of fixation and any other point in space depends on the disparity between the two retinal images of those points. In a schematic mechanistic sense, the sensation of depth appears to arise from a psychic appreciation of the number of subjective direction units corresponding to the number of retinal elements between the fovea and the image in one eye compared to that in the other eye."

The convergence theory accounted for binocular depth by having the eyes scan the region being viewed, at each point obtaining the distance by triangulation. The disparity theory calls for the appearance of depth to be directly related to a difference between the images on the two retinae, without regard to the direction of pointing of the eyes.

However, at this point a curious contradiction enters. Although the definition of binocular disparity does not refer to the direction of pointing of the eyes, the geometric treatment of disparity almost always implies it. Wheatstone originally asked, what are the disparities introduced or what is the difference between the images produced by a particular object. Helmholtz sought the geometric statement of the disparity between two given points. Continuing to the present day, the problem is usually put in terms of defining the disparities produced by a given external configuration. But as soon as one specifies a particular configuration in a definite spatial relation to the observer, the geometry is fixed and includes, no matter how one disguises it, the convergence angles of the eyes. We can describe this as reasoning from the object to the observer. It represents a perfectly legitimate way of dealing with the problem and it has yielded important and productive results. But it is only one possible approach, and not the only or the necessary one.

THE CONTRIBUTION OF AMES

The fundamental contribution of Ames to perceptual theory lies in the fact that he asked an old question in a new way. The time-honored question of space perception had always been, "Given the physical world, what is the related percept?" Ames, faced with crucial observation, reversed this question. "Given a perception, what is the related physical world?" The difference between these two questions is monumental. One reasons from the "outside in," the other from the "inside out." One takes the external physical world as its point of departure, the other takes the experiencing individual as the center of its study. The entire approach to space perception presented in Ames' work follows directly from the new way in which he posed the underlying question.

Ames was led to this approach through his study of binocular stereopsis. As we have seen, since Wheatstone first propounded it, the question was always asked, "Given a physical arrangement, what are the attendant disparities?" Ames asked the inverse question, "Given a particular disparity, what is the accompanying physical arrangement?" He was led to this question through observations made in his study of aniseikonia.

Briefly, and grossly simplified, these observations were two-fold. First, in working with aniseikonic patients, Ames was struck by the fact that even people with fairly extreme cases of aniseikonia were normally able to function visually quite effectively. Frequently they were unaware of any perceptual anomalies, experiencing instead headaches and other signs of discomfort. Intrigued by this observation, Ames set about wearing glasses which induced in him various forms of aniseikonia and systematically recorded his observations. He published a detailed account, the basic conclusion of which can be briefly summarized. Ames found that, from a knowledge of the geometric optical distortions introduced, he could not predict what he would experience perceptually. For example, he found that, while wearing the same pair of lenses, he would perceive quite different distortions depending on what he was looking at. He concluded that what he perceived depended on at least two factors in addition to the type of glasses he was wearing. These were: (1) Subjective assumptions as to the nature of the surface he was looking at. For example, looking at a lawn, he saw the lawn tilted. Wearing the same glasses but looking at a lake, he saw the lake farther away but horizontal.

(2) The presence or absence of conflicting monocular cues. For example, the lawn might appear tilted, whereas wearing the same glasses indoors everything appeared normal (cf. Wheatstone and the pseudoscope).

These observations led him to propose, first, the existence of binocularly equivalent configurations and, second, the close interrelationship between binocular and monocular cues. We turn now to an elaboration of the first proposition.

BINOCULARLY EQUIVALENT CONFIGURATIONS

Ames' hypothesis of binocularly equivalent configurations was in its essentials quite simple. Since the same disparities could be seen as a sloping lawn nearby or a horizontal lake far away, may it not be possible that, physically, a near tilted surface and a far level surface produce the same disparity? Or, asking the question more rigorously, if we assume a given disparity, what physical surface or surfaces will provide this disparity? Note that this question specifically omits any reference to convergence, and Ames' definition of binocularly equivalent configurations depends on the assumption that stereoscopic depth is independent of convergence. There is

evidence that, strictly speaking, this assumption is not true, but it
holds at least as a first-order approximation.

Referring to Figure VII-3

$$\eta = \text{Disparity} = \alpha_2 - \alpha_1 = \theta_1 - \theta_2. \qquad \text{VII--1}$$

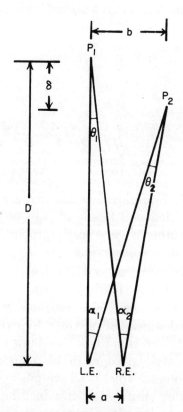

Figure VII-3   Geometry of binocular disparity when the two points and the eyes all lie in
the horizontal plane.

It is generally agreed that binocular disparity provides a cue to
the distance of objects relative to each other and not of their absolute distances, i.e., relative to the observer. For example, Fry has
written that, "although stereopsis aids one in judging the relative
distances of two or more objects, it does not give any information
about the absolute distance of the objects." Similarly, Ogle states,
"the angles α_1 and α_2 themselves (corresponding to retinal dimen-

Ogle
Relative
depth
only
from α of
i

sions) do not provide sufficient means for the judgment of the *absolute* distance of either F or P from the eyes, but their difference does provide the stimulus for the relative *localization* (depth) of the two points." This fact immediately suggests the possibility of stereoptically equivalent configurations, which can easily be verified. If we assume in Figure VII-3 that δ, a, and b are all $\ll D$,

$$\theta_1 = \frac{a}{D}$$

$$\theta_2 = \frac{a}{D - \delta}$$

$$\eta = \theta_1 - \theta_2 = \frac{a}{D} - \frac{a}{D - \delta} = \frac{a\delta}{D(D - \delta)}$$

$$\eta \cong \frac{a\delta}{D^2}. \qquad\qquad \text{VII–2}$$

It follows directly from this equation that a given binocular disparity, η = constant, defines a family of pairs of points whose spacing relative to each other is very nearly proportional to the square of their distance from the observer.

It is possible, however, to establish a more general, and more rigorous, statement of binocularly equivalent configurations. The following presentation is condensed and modified from Luneburg.

The mathematical statement of Ames' hypothesis, which is outlined below, is taken directly from Luneburg and is achieved by him in the first twenty-five pages of his monograph. This much, which seems to be unassailable, is all we are here concerned with. The remainder of Luneburg's work, in which he derives his hyperbolic metric for binocular space, represents his own contribution and is much more controversial. It has been seriously criticized by Ogle and Fry, and direct experimental tests by Hardy and his coworkers have proved inconclusive.

However, this is no intention to imply that the following derivation represents the only, or the best, way of deriving binocularly equivalent configurations. It is one way of doing it. Other derivations have been based on somewhat different assumptions. It is still too early to decide conclusively what is the best way of dealing with binocularly equivalent configurations. The following treatment shows, at the very least, that it is possible without invoking unduly limiting assumptions to derive such configurations. Furthermore, this derivation provides new and useful ways of handling old problems, as will be shown at the end of the chapter.

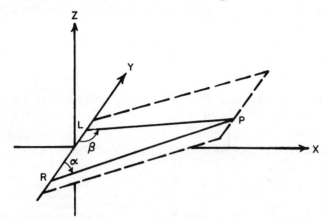

Figure VII-4 Rectangular and polar coordinates for the general geometry of binocular disparity (after Luneburg).

In the coordinate system indicated in Figure VII-4, let us consider an observer with his eyes located at the points $y = \pm 1$. In Cartesian coordinates, a point P can be characterized by x,y,z. We now introduce a bipolar coordinate system in which θ is the angle of elevation of the plane through the y axis and the point P, and α and β are the angles between the y axis and lines drawn to P from the right and left eye, respectively. The positive directions of α and β are as indicated in the figure.

The relation between the x,y,z coordinates and the α, β, θ coordinates is given by

$$x = \frac{2 \cos \theta}{\cot \alpha + \cot \beta} \quad , \quad \cot \alpha = \frac{y + 1}{\sqrt{x^2 + z^2}}$$

$$y = \frac{\cot \alpha - \cot \beta}{\cot \alpha + \cot \beta} \quad , \quad \cot \beta = \frac{1 - y}{\sqrt{x^2 + z^2}} \qquad \text{VII–3}$$

$$z = \frac{2 \sin \theta}{\cot \alpha + \cot \beta} \quad , \quad \cot \theta = \frac{x}{z} .$$

We now consider a line element (dx, dy, dz) attached to point P. It will be projected on the right retina as a line element $(d\alpha, d\theta)$

and on the left retina as $(-d\beta, d\theta)$. The physiological significance of this is clear: $d\alpha + d\beta$ represents the horizontal disparity of the line element (dx, dy, dz).

It follows that two line elements in space (dx_1, dy_1, dz_1) and (dx_2, dy_2, dz_2) will present identical binocular indications if

$$d\alpha_1 = d\alpha_2$$
$$d\beta_1 = d\beta_2$$
$$d\theta_1 = d\theta_2.$$

Such line elements are *binocularly equivalent*. Furthermore, since most external objects can be considered as configurations of line elements, this is readily generalized to curves and surfaces. It is evident that the transformation

$$\alpha' = \alpha + \delta$$
$$\beta' = \beta + \epsilon \qquad\qquad \text{VII–4}$$
$$\theta' = \theta + \lambda$$

satisfies the conditions for binocular equivalence. Hence, any two surfaces in space such that one can be transformed into the other by transformation of this type are *binocularly equivalent surfaces*.

In general, this simple transformation in the α, β, θ coordinate system leads to a complex transformation in the x,y,z, coordinates. We shall illustrate this with one simple, but by no means trivial, example. Let the problem be to determine the curves which are equivalent to the straight line $x = x_o$ lying in the xy plane.

We first introduce the new coordinates

$$v = \pi - \alpha - \beta$$
$$\phi = \tfrac{1}{2}(\beta - \alpha)$$
$$\theta = \theta$$

which retain the physiological significance of the α,β,θ coordinates, $-dv = d\alpha + d\beta$ being the binocular disparity.

The transformation

$$v' = v + \tau$$
$$\phi' = \phi + \sigma$$
$$\theta' = \theta + \lambda$$

satisfies the conditions for binocular equivalence or, in other words, binocular disparity is invariant with respect to this transformation.

It is easily shown that, in the xy plane, the relation between the x, y coordinates and v, ϕ coordinates is given approximately (i.e., for distances large compared to the interpupilary distance) by

$$v = \frac{2x}{x^2 + y^2}$$

$$\tan \phi = \frac{y}{x}.$$

Applying the transformation

$$v' = v + \tau$$
$$\phi = \phi$$

we obtain

$$\frac{x'}{x'^2 + y'^2} = \frac{x}{x^2 + y^2} + \frac{\tau}{2}$$

$$\frac{y'}{x'} = \frac{y}{x}.$$

Substituting $y' = \frac{yx'}{x}$ in the first equation leads directly to

$$x = x' \left(1 + \frac{\tau}{2} \frac{x^2 + y^2}{x} \right). \qquad \text{VII–5}$$

The inversion of this formula is obtained simply by replacing τ by $-\tau$.

$$x' = x \left(1 - \frac{\tau}{2} \frac{x'^2 + y'^2}{x'} \right).$$

Since we are concerned with the transformation of the line $x = x_0$, we can write directly (substituting x, y for x', y')

$$x = x_0 \left(1 - \frac{\tau}{2} \frac{x^2 + y^2}{x} \right). \qquad \text{VII–6}$$

Hence the straight line $x = x_0$ transforms into a family of binocularly equivalent conic sections, hyperbolae if $\tau < 0$ and ellipses if $\tau > 0$.

THREE SPECIAL PROBLEMS IN BINOCULAR SPACE PERCEPTION

I. An hypothesis concerning the apparent frontoparallel plane horopter

The empirical frontoparallel plane horopter at near distances is generally considered to be a curve, concave toward the observer, lying somewhere between the Vieth-Müller circle and the objective frontoparallel plane. As viewing distance increases, the curve becomes progressively flatter until a distance is reached at which it coincides with the objective frontoparallel plane. Beyond this distance it is convex toward the observer. Ogle has provided us with the most complete and definitive discussion of this subject. Using a measure, H, of the curvature of the horopter at the fixation point, he has shown that H is not constant, as would be predicted on the assumption of constant functional disparity between the two retinae, but increases markedly as fixation distance decreases. Ogle points out that, while one can not at this time ascertain the basis for this change in H, "it is a consistent and regular process." He further indicates that it is difficult on optical grounds to "account for the difference between the nonius and the apparent frontoparallel plane data," while "from a teleological point of view we might ask why the apparent frontoparallel plane deviates at all from the objective frontoparallel plane." Some light may be thrown on these problems of the empirical frontoparallel plane horopter by introducing the concept of equivalent configurations.

If we assume that binocular disparity provides information only of relative distances from the observer and not of absolute distance, we can not, at the same time, assume that the apparent frontoparallel plane is necessarily seen at the fixation distance. It, therefore, becomes reasonable to ask if there may not exist at some other distance an objective frontoparallel plane which provides the same disparities as the empirically determined curves. This is a problem in *binocularly equivalent surfaces*. Two surfaces as we have seen can be defined as binocularly equivalent if, for every line element ds_1 on one surface, there exists a corresponding line element ds_2 on the other surface such that ds_1 and ds_2 provide on the retinae the same horizontal disparity, the same lateral extension, and the same vertical extension.

We have shown that for every objective frontoparallel plane

$x = x_0$ there exists a binocularly equivalent family of surfaces whose intersection with the horizontal plane through the eyes is given approximately by Equation VII-6,

$$x = x_o \left(1 - \frac{\tau}{2} \frac{x^2 + y^2}{x}\right)$$

with τ as an arbitrary parameter.

Our problem now becomes the relatively simple one of ascertaining whether this equation, with unique values of x_o and τ, fits the data for the empirical frontoparallel plane horopter at a given fixation distance. Figure VII-5 shows the curve which is equivalent to an objective frontoparallel plane at $x_o = 30$ cm, $\tau = 0.0083$, together with the data for one observer at a fixation distance of 20 cm, taken from Ogle. The mathematical curve fits the data reasonably well. Similarly satisfactory fits can be obtained for other data given in Ogle.

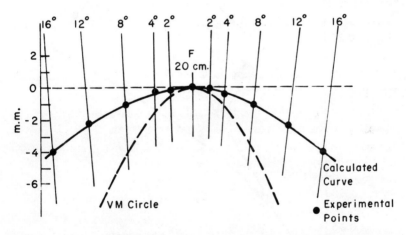

Figure VII-5   Fronto-parallel plane at fixation distance of 20cm (experimental data from Ogle) compared with calculated curve.

We may now ask whether the hypothesis of a binocularly equivalent objective frontoparallel plane lying somewhat behind the empirical apparent frontoparallel plane can account for the observed change in H with observation distance. Let us assume that this

hypothetical objective frontoparallel plane lies a constant distance
of 10 cm behind the fixation distance. This assumption is obviously
not justified, since it would have the empirical and objective frontoparallel planes coinciding only at infinity, whereas in point of fact
they correspond at some near distance beyond which the empirical
curve becomes convex toward the observer. This difficulty, however,
is not so great as it may seem. For negative values of τ the plane
$x = x_0$ lies in front of the family of equivalent curves, which are
convex toward the observer. Hence, the discrepancy can be taken
care of by assuming a critical distance beyond which x_0 is less than
the fixation distance. There seems little to be gained at this point,
however, by complicating the calculations with such an assumption.

It then becomes a simple matter to calculate H. In Figure VII-6
this calculated curve of H is shown together with the data for three

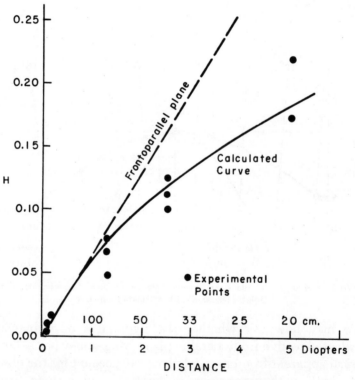

Figure VII-6 Experimental values of H (data from Ogle) compared with calculated curve.

observers, again taken from Ogle. We note satisfactory agreement between the predicted curve and the measured data.

It would appear from our discussion that the data obtained for the apparent frontoparallel plane horopter are consistent with the assumption of an objective frontoparallel plane lying somewhat behind the empirical curve and binocularly equivalent to it. It is recognized that such an hypothesis is incomplete and probably raises more questions than it can hope to answer. Mathematically, however, it would seem to be justified. Whether or not it has any physiological or psychological meaning is a matter for empirical determination. In any event, it is comforting both optically and teleologically to know that there exists an objective frontoparallel plane to which the empirically determined horopter is binocularly equivalent.

2. The wall paper phenomenon

The wall paper experiment was first reported well over one hundred years ago. Briefly, an observer stands a few feet distant from, and squarely facing, a wall covered with a regular, repeating pattern of small figures. By increasing the convergence of his eyes while observing the pattern on the wall, the observer will note that there are one or more amounts of convergence for which fusion will be obtained, but with different, rather than the same, parts of the pattern fusing together. At the same time, the entire wall will appear to have moved nearer to the observer and become smaller. The same effect has been reported for a typewriter keyboard, two postage stamps, and various other repeated figures. When a caned chair seat is used, the middle of the seat appears to bow upward out of its frame. We can observe the opposite effect when looking through a chain fence, for example, and converging beyond it. Not all observers experience these effects all of the time, but the effects are of sufficiently regular occurrence to merit attention.

The wall paper experiment was first explained by assuming that the convergence of the eyes provided an indication of the apparent distance of the wall. In the one hundred years since this explanation was first offered, experiment after experiment has shown that convergence is at best a very low-order depth indication, certainly not capable of moving walls. Nevertheless, current writers continue to account for the wall paper effect on the basis of convergence, *faute de mieux*. It will here be shown that the wall paper effect can be completely accounted for in terms of binocular disparities, thereby taking it out of the realm of convergence and onto the solid ground of stereopsis.

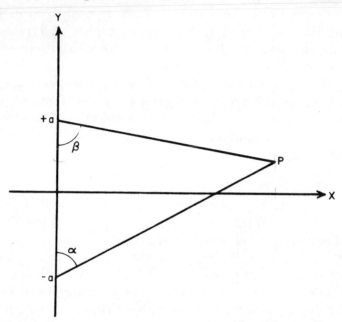

Figure VII-7   Rectangular and polar coordinates for horizontal plane passing the eyes.

The mathematical demonstration of this result is straightforward. In Figure VII-7, a point P can be characterized by the Cartesian coordinates (x, y) or by the bipolar coordinates (α, β). The relation between these coordinates is given by

$$\cot \alpha = \frac{a + y}{x}$$

$$\cot \beta = \frac{a - y}{x}.$$

If the eyes are placed on the y axis at points $y = \pm a$, as indicated in the figure, it is clear that the geometric disparity of a line element (dx, dy) attached to the point P is given by $d\alpha + d\beta$, which may be found by differentiating the above equations.

Now, letting P lie on the straight line $x = x_o$, differentiating and adding, we obtain an expression for the disparity of an element dy on this line at the point y.

$$d\alpha + d\beta = x_o \left[\frac{1}{x_o{}^2 + (a - y)^2} - \frac{1}{x_o{}^2 + (a + y)^2} \right] \qquad \text{VII–7}$$

We now converge the eyes symetrically to some distance C, less than x_o, so that the two points, P_R (x_o, y_o) projected on to the right fovea and P_L $(x_o, -y_o)$ projected on to the left fovea, fuse, as shown in Figure VII-8.

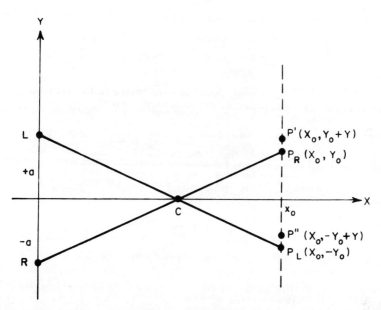

Figure VII-8   The "wall-paper" phenomenon. With the eyes converged on point C, P_R and P_L are identical parts of the pattern falling on the right and left fovea respectively. P' and P" are identical parts of the pattern falling on disparate parts of the two retinae.

The two points P' and P", projected on to the right and left fovea respectively, represent corresponding parts of the wall paper pattern. Our problem is to find the disparity associated with a line element dy' attached to P' and dy'' attached to P". Since P' is located at point $(x_o, y_o + Y)$ and P" at $(x_o, -y_o + Y)$, we write immediately

$$\cot \alpha = \frac{a + y_o + Y}{x_o}$$

$$\cot \beta = \frac{a + y_o - Y}{x_o}.$$

Differentiating and adding we find the binocular disparity of line element dY given by

$$d\alpha + d\beta = x_o \left[\frac{1}{x_o{}^2 + (a + y_o - Y)^2} - \frac{1}{x_o{}^2 + (a + y_o + Y)^2} \right]. \quad \text{VII–8}$$

A comparison between these equations and the corresponding equations derived immediately previously shows that the disparities under conditions of increased convergence are exactly the same as would result from placing the eyes at points $y = \pm(a + y_o)$, that is, multiplying the interpupillary distance by $\dfrac{a + y_o}{a}$. This result becomes obvious from Figure VII-8 if one moves the triangles LP_LP'' and RP_RP' up and down respectively until P_L and P_R coincide with the x axis.

The separation of the eyes, of course, remains constant during the process of convergence. The same result, however, can be obtained by multiplying all dimensions by $\dfrac{a}{a + y_o}$ resulting in

$$d\alpha + d\beta = \frac{a}{a + y_o} x_o \left[\frac{1}{\left(\dfrac{a}{a + y_o}\right)^2 x_o{}^2 + \left(a + \dfrac{aY}{a + y_o}\right)^2} - \right.$$

$$\left. \frac{1}{\left(\dfrac{a}{a + y_o}\right)^2 x_o{}^2 + \left(a - \dfrac{aY}{a + y_o}\right)^2} \right]. \qquad \text{VII–9}$$

From this it follows that the straight line at distance x_o becomes a new straight line at distance $\dfrac{a}{a + y_o} x_0$ and that a length $\triangle Y$ on the original line becomes a new length $\dfrac{a}{a + y_o} \triangle Y$.

Since the distance of convergence $x_c = \dfrac{a}{a + y_o} x_0$, this leads to the interesting conclusion that the transformed line is seen at the convergence distance.

Ames has reported two tests of this derivation, both of which yielded positive results. First, if a surface with a repeating pattern is curved to form an arc of a circle and the observer is placed so that his two eyes also fall on the circumference of the same circle, we have the conditions for the Vieth-Müller circle. Disparities in this case remain unchanged with changing convergence. Thus, the convergence theory would predict the wallpaper effect to occur with changes in convergence while the disparity theory would not. Observations under these conditions indicate no effect of changing convergence.

A second, and opposite, approach can be made by using prisms to change the parts of the repeating pattern which are fused without changing the actual convergence of the eyes. The convergence theory predicts no change while the disparity theory predicts the wallpaper effect. Observers under these conditions report the wallpaper effect.

3. The binocular distorted rooms

Binocular distorted rooms are examples of equivalent configurations in which all the cues normally available to a stationary observer are utilized. It will be shown that two such equivalent configurations, which are grossly different in their physical properties, are nevertheless indistinguishable to an observer who has no additional information concerning them.

The principles for designing binocular distorted rooms have already been indicated in the discussion of binocularly equivalent configurations. Two binocular distorted rooms were computed and constructed, one an "interior" room, i.e., of dimensions smaller than those of the reference room; and one an "exterior" room, i.e., of dimensions larger than those of the reference room. Mathematically, these two rooms are represented by positive and negative values of τ in the transformation equation.

The surfaces from which these rooms are formed are complex, three-dimensional curves. The task of constructing such surfaces proved to be quite difficult and was finally solved by enlisting the aid of a shipbuilding concern. The rooms are, literally, built like a ship, with the curves cut in vertical and horizontal members and plywood bent and molded to these members. A third, rectangular room of the dimensions of the reference room was also constructed.

It was predicted, as already stated, that these three rooms would appear identical, which in practice reduces to the prediction that the two distorted rooms will look like the same rectangular room.

When the rooms were initially assembled, they were painted a uniform, neutral color. In this condition they were viewed by the author and others, all of whom had been working with the rooms. Both rooms appeared to be rectangular, but they appeared to be of quite different sizes, which closely approximated their actual sizes. It was concluded that this partial failure of the prediction might be due to the fact that such factors as the grain of the wood, nail heads, dirt marks, etc., did not conform to the criteria for equivalence. This difficulty could not be overcome by providing the surfaces with a perfectly uniform, flawless covering, since this would at the same time remove all stereoscopic stimuli, except from the intersections of the surfaces.

It was decided to paint identical patterns on both rooms, and simulated floor boards, sills, windows, window frames, etc., were provided. Whether this rather laborious step was essential remains doubtful. When the same observers now viewed the rooms from the proper position, the same results were obtained. Both rooms appeared rectangular, but again approximately their true sizes.

The rooms were then shown to five observers who had no knowledge of the nature or aims of the experiment. Each observer was blindfolded and led to the "interior" room. A headrest was provided which prevented him from seeing anything other than the room itself. When the observer's head was in the rest, the blindfold was removed and he was asked to describe what he saw. No further questions were asked except, "Anything else?" When the subject had exhausted his description, he was again blindfolded, and the experiment was repeated with the "exterior" room. He was again blindfolded while he was being led away from the rooms, after which he was interviewed searchingly with respect to the apparent sizes and shapes of the rooms. The above viewing procedure was then repeated, with the exception that the observer was now questioned about the size and shape of each room while he was viewing it; such comments as "are you sure?" and "make absolutely certain" were used.

On the first viewing there were no important differences in the appearance of the two rooms. No difference in shape was reported by any observer, either in the first viewing or during the interview. One observer reported a slight size difference which he later repudiated, and one observer reported a size difference in a direction opposite to that of the actual difference. The remaining three observers reported minor size differences in the direction of the actual difference. The reported magnitudes of these differences, one foot and two feet, are considerably smaller than the actual difference which is of the order of six feet.

The reports on the second viewing show that slight shape distortion of the "exterior" room was apparent to two observers. In addition, two observers reported small size differences and two reported major size differences, all in the direction of the actual difference. Only one observer did not change his report on the second viewing.

The results following the second viewing have not been replicated, and it can not be stated whether they are due to a "critical" viewing attitude or to an experimental artifact. The findings on the initial viewing have, however, been repeated and appear to be reliable. It is possible to summarize what seem to be the well established reactions of observers to the binocular distorted rooms as follows:

a. Subjects who are led to the rooms blindfolded, with precautions taken to avoid any sensory indications of the sizes of the rooms, report that the two rooms appear substantially identical, i.e., rectangular rooms of the same size.

b. Subjects who catch even a glimpse of the exterior dimensions of the rooms report them to be rectangular but of different sizes which closely approximate their true sizes.

c. Even complete familiarity with the rooms, such as that of the author and others who worked intimately with them, results in only occasional and minor deviations from apparent rectangularity.

VIII

Accommodation
and Convergence

There remains a group of cues which do not fit into any of the categories so far studied, and yet which must be considered in any study of visual space perception. They are usually referred to as kinesthetic cues since the information utilized for visual space perception comes from body movements rather than from retinal stimulation. This terminology is somewhat restricting, and the broader term, "non-visual cues," may be more useful. It would refer to all cues utilized in visual perception that do not directly involve retinal stimulation. This broader term encompasses not only accommodation and convergence, which will be treated in this book, but also a number of other non-visual cues that have important consequences for visual space perception. Notable among these are the ego-centric localization of the observer and the direction of objects from him relative to this localization. Less directly relevant but equally interesting are auditory and haptic space perception, both as topics in their own right and in their complex interrelationship with visual space cues.

Accommodation and convergence as non-visual cues to visual space perception occupy a rather shaky position. Both of these factors provide possible visual cues, blurring and double images, but, as we have seen, it is not feasible to separate their visual from their non-visual aspects experimentally.

The presumed way in which accommodation functions as a depth cue is usually likened to the focusing of a (reflex) camera. The camera lens is adjusted until a sharp picture of the object in question is obtained. The distance of the object can then be computed from a knowledge of the characteristics of the lens and a measure of the distance from the lens to the surface on which the image is focused. Or, more simply, the distance can be read directly from a scale which has previously been calibrated. Exactly so with the eye, the argument runs. The lens of the eye is adjusted for a sharp picture on the retina, and the muscular effort involved in making this adjustment is, figuratively, checked against a calibrated scale reading directly in distance.

The presumed functioning of convergence as a depth cue is, in an analogous way, likened to the technique of a surveyor. He first lays off a base line of fixed length, and then at each end of this base line measures the angle between the base line and a line drawn to any distant object. From a knowledge of these two angles and the length of the base line, he can readily compute the distance of the object. Or, if the length of the base line remains fixed, he can read the distance directly from a calibrated table once he knows the two angles. Again, runs the argument, exactly so with the eyes. The distance between the eyes provides a fixed base line, and the muscular efforts involved in directing the two eyes toward an object so that only a single image is obtained provide measures of the angles involved. These muscular efforts can, again figuratively, be entered into a table and the distance read directly.

For some reason, most of the writers who described accommodation and convergence as distance cues this way seem to feel that such "conversion tables" are built into the organism in much the same way that a camera or a range-finder one buys has a distance scale already marked on it. But the argument is actually independent of whether the organism comes already calibrated or calibrates itself through experience. In either event, once calibrated, accommodation and convergence, according to this view, provide accurate and reliable measures of the distances of objects about us, and, furthermore, these measures are independent of any confusing psychological variables. The argument is precise, rigorous and flawless. The only obstacle to its acceptance is the fact that a century of experimentation has failed to provide any evidence that it describes what actually occurs.

Why, then, do we still encounter writers who insist on adhering to what we will call the "rationalistic account" of accommodation and convergence? The answer is probably to be found in the history of the subject. It is striking that, in sharp contradistinction to what happened with all the visual cues, the rationalistic account of accommodation and convergence was arrived at independent of any observation or experimentation. We have seen that there have been two major epochs of discovery of the visual cues. One, starting in antiquity and culminating in the Greco-Roman period, saw the discovery of those depth cues which are available to the pictorial artist. There have been elaborations, technical improvements, and conceptual refinements ever since, but it is safe to say that there are no depth cues available to the pictorial artist today which cannot be found exemplified in work dating prior to the first century A.D. The second great epoch of discovery stemmed from a growing interest of the natural sciences in the meaning and nature of observation. It started in the mid-nineteenth century and continues to the present day; it is closely linked to the experimental laboratory. Accommodation and convergence do not belong to either of these epochs. They do not stem from the harsh demands of the artist's canvas or the scientist's laboratory. Their genesis lies in rational thought unencumbered by observation.

The general argument with respect to accommodation and convergence has always run something like this: "Here are two perfectly good means for measuring distance. It is intolerable to think that the creator did not make use of them." This is an excellent example of the so-called "pathetic fallacy," i.e., it must be true because the thought of it not being true is intolerable.

THE PROBLEMS OF ACCOMMODATION AND CONVERGENCE

The fact that the rationalistic account has not stood the test of experiment does not mean that we can exclude accommodation and convergence in a study of visual space perception. They probably do not function as visual distance cues in the rationalistic way but they are interrelated with apparent distance in a manner that makes their study interesting and rewarding. In the following discussion we will not consider physiological problems nor are we going into clinical ophthalmology and optometry and their concern with anomalies of accommodation and convergence, except where directly relevant to our study. We will concentrate on the psychologically important aspects of accommodation and convergence in their relationship to apparent distance. Three pertinent questions can be asked: (1) What is the effect of change of accommodation and convergence on apparent distance, i.e., do accommodation and convergence act as cues to distance? (2) What is the effect of change of actual distance on accommodation and convergence, i.e., to what extent do the eyes accommodate and converge for the actual distance of the object of regard? (3) What is the effect of change of apparent distance on accommodation and convergence, i.e., do apparent "nearness" and apparent "farness" influence accommodation and convergence? These questions are obviously not mutually exclusive; none of them can be experimentally answered without knowing or controlling the effects related to the other two. In practice, however, most experiments have been primarily directed at answering only one of these questions, and our discussion of the evidence will be divided correspondingly.

Experimental variables

Before discussing the evidence, we will briefly indicate the requirements for an adequate experimental approach. There are four major variables which need to be controlled or measured. If data with respect to any one of these are lacking, conclusions drawn from the experimental finding are open to question.

Apparent distance. In general, apparent distance is a subjective datum which cannot be observed or measured directly by the experimenter. However, it can be approached in two ways. First, an equivalent apparent distance can be measured; or, second, if the object is viewed in a familiar well-structured situation, it can simply be assumed that apparent localization is approximately equal to its physical localization. Both of these techniques of arriving at apparent distance have been utilized satisfactorily.

Actual condition of accommodation and convergence. This can be measured in one of two ways. A number of instruments have been devised for the direct measurement of accommodation and convergence. In addition to direct instrumental measurement, it is possible to use the measured distance of the object plus the characteristics of any lenses that may be used, provided there is a clear indication that the object in question is in sharp focus. Simply knowing the measured distance of the object but lacking the evidence of sharp focus is not sufficient to determine the distance for which the eyes are accommodated and converged.

Physical distance of the object. The physical distance of the object of regard enters into the problem in two quite distinct ways. First, it determines the optical properties of the light (traveling from the object to the eye) which together with the state of accommodation and convergence determines the characteristics of the retinal images. Second, the physical distance of the object may be related to its apparent distance; however, this relationship is often quite tenuous, and any work which uncritically assumes actual and apparent distance to be equal is open to doubt.

The visual distance cues. Any experimenter interested in studying the role of accommodation and convergence as indications of distance must know, for proper interpretation, whether or not any other visual distance cues are operative.

Unfortunately, many experiments do not provide all the needed data about the four major variables. Broadly speaking, apparent distance has been dealt with mainly by psychologists, who frequently neglect the measurement of accommodation and convergence. The actual condition of accommodation and convergence has largely been approached by ophthalmologists and optometrists, who frequently neglect measurements of apparent distance. In general, experiments dealing with the effect of apparent distance on accommodation and convergence are usually adequate in providing all the data. But as we shall see, this is an area which has received very little experimental treatment.

I. Accommodation and convergence as cues to distance

The first experiment on accommodation as a cue to distance was performed by Wundt. He had his observer view a vertical thread under such conditions that accommodation was presumably the only cue to its distance. He then moved the thread either toward or away from the observer who reported any change in apparent distance. Correct reports were presumed to be evidence of utilization of accommodation as a distance cue. This early experiment is representative of the general procedure followed in all later work, the chief addition being the use of binocular observation in which convergence is controlled by forcing fusion of the images for some distance other than the actual distance. The mirror stereoscope of Carr and its modification by Grant may be taken as examples.

Most recent work has further attempted to study accommodation and convergence as cues to absolute distance from the observer, as well as to changes in this distance. In general, the effort is made, as in all previous work, first, to eliminate by *a priori* considerations all cues to distance other than accommodation and convergence, and second, to find whether distance can be judged under these conditions.

Out of the welter of conflicting results from these experiments, there seems to emerge general agreement that (a) accommodation and convergence can function as cues to apparent distance, and (b) their effectiveness in this role varies from primary to minor to virtually non-existent. A statement from Boring, Langfeld and Weld of what may be regarded as a typical position on this question holds that "accurate vision involves constant motor adjustment of the eyes to the distances of the stimulating objects. . . . This adjustment requires a pattern of muscular contractions and tensions characteristic of every distance. It is generally believed that these contractions and tensions give rise to proprioceptive clues to the distance of the fixated object."

While we will not take exception here to this conclusion, it is imperative to question much of the experimentation on which it is based. All reported work has explicitly or implicitly assumed *a priori* answers to the other two pertinent problems, answers which are either unproven or invalid. Specifically, it assumed that apparent distance has no effect on accommodation and convergence, and that the eyes are in fact always accommodated and converged for the actual distance of the object of regard. Grant, for example, states that "for objects 'within infinity,' which by optical convention means within six meters, accommodation and convergence vary in amount with the distance of the object." Let us consider evidence of the validity of this assumption.

2. Actual distance as a determinant of accommodation and convergence

It is generally agreed that the function of accommodation and convergence is to produce a sharp image on the foveal region of each retina. This requires accommodating and converging for the actual distance of the stimulus object. There is an extensive literature, chiefly reported in ophthalmological and optometrical journals, in which the distance of accommodation and convergence has been most carefully measured and correlated with the actual distance of the stimulus. The findings indicate that in binocular vision fusion generally forces convergence to the actual distance of the viewed object, within the limits of fixation disparity. This term has been used to refer to the fact that under certain conditions a single, fused image will be experienced although "the retinal images of the point of fixation may be actually disparate." However, both binocular and monocular accommodation as well as convergence in monocular observation can, and frequently do, differ quite widely from that required for the actual distance. Indeed, much of the work in clinical refraction has always been devoted to attempts to correct anomalies occurring when these mechanisms for one reason or another do not perform their functions properly. Extreme examples of such anomalies are squint, in which one eye is radically diverged from the point of view of the other eye, and cases in which accommodation is for distances other than the actual distance, which can reach the point of causing severe pathology. A lack of correspondence between distance of accommodation and actual distance even for normal observers was pointed out by Ames and Gliddon, who concluded that in most cases actual distance and accommodation distance coincide at only one point.

These and other anomalies, together with the findings for normal eyes, force us to conclude that it is unwise to assume that the condition of the image-producing mechanisms can be determined solely from a knowledge of the distance of the stimulus, and that any experimental findings based on such an assumption must be open to doubt. However, much of the work on which this conclusion is based itself neglects the possible role of apparent distance as a determinant of accommodation and convergence.

3. Apparent distance as a determinant of accommodation and convergence

This problem has received but little mention and virtually no systematic study. Most writers leave the question open by implying but never explicitly discussing it. A typical statement says that "it appears that the three innervations (for accommodation, convergence, and pupillary contraction) . . . are released by the impulse for clear vision of near objects." Here "clearness" and "nearness" are both mentioned, and, since no distinction is made between actual and apparent nearness, the statement would seem to reflect general uncertainty as to the role of apparent distance in controlling accommodation and convergence.

There is, nevertheless, some evidence on this question. Luckiesh and Moss claim that "the proximity of the hand to the eyes when operating the sensitometer may tend to stimulate accommodation reflexly due to the impression of 'nearness' arising from proprioceptor phenomena." Elsewhere, under the heading "a paradox of accommodation," these same authors assert that "when an observer looks at a two-dimensional picture of a three-dimensional scene, such as landscape, changes in accommodation not infrequently take place as different parts of the picture are viewed, notwithstanding the fact that all parts of the picture would be in focus for the same accommodation." Unfortunately, Luckiesh and Moss do not cite any reference or data for this interesting observation, and most other recent writers would seem to disagree with them. Walls, for example, holds that "the stimulus to converge seems to be the psychic impression of nearness," but makes no such claim about accommodation, which he thinks is controlled by the need for sharp focus.

The most extensive recent experimental study of this question is that of Hofstetter, to which the reader is referred for a detailed discussion and history. Hofstetter presented similar targets monocularly at two distances, 5 meters and 0.345 meters, and varied the demands on accommodation by means of lenses. Apparent distance was not measured but was considered determined by the relation of the targets to other visible parts of the room. Haploscopic measures of accommodation and convergence were taken. Hofstetter concludes that "awareness of nearness of the point of fixation is effective in bringing about changes in convergence," but "the data provides no evidence for proximal accommodation." This is modified, however, by the statement that "the failure to obtain evidence of proximal accommodation can probably be attributed to the fact that the subjects were experienced in the use of optical instruments and had previously performed a number of experiments that dealt with the problems of accommodation."

Similar conclusions were reached by Morgan on the basis of a very similar approach. He states that "the psychic influence of the subject's awareness of the nearness of objects has little influence upon accommodation, but it does influence convergence."

Ohwaki, using a technique involving measuring the sizes of after images concluded that "accommodation depends on perceived distance rather than physical distance."

Ittelson and Ames made the following direct experimental approach to the problem.

a. *Static size change—monocular.*   Different sizes of a familiar object (playing card) were presented one at a time at a distance of 32 inches. Measures of apparent distance, accommodation, and convergence were taken. For four out of five observers, apparent distance of the double-size card was an average of one-fourth that of the half-size card; accommodation when viewing the double-size card was an average of .25 diopters nearer than when viewing the half-size card, and convergence followed the same pattern.

b. *Continuous size change—monocular.*   The projected image of a playing card which continuously changed size from normal to one-third size was viewed from a distance of 16 inches. Introspective reports of four observers indicated that apparent distance changed continuously with the size of the image, the card appearing to move back and forth as it grew smaller and larger. Measures of accommodation showed an average of .46 diopters nearer for the large size than for the small size. Convergence measurements indicated similar results.

c. *Continuous size change—binocular.*   The same stimulus configuration was used as above. Introspective reports indicated a distinct impression of movement. Some blurring of the images suggests a shift in accommodation. Severe feelings of muscular strain about the eyes were reported after a few minutes.

"The specific experimental problem posed was that of determining whether a change in apparent distance alone will induce a change in accommodation and convergence. The results of the experiments reported above suggest an affirmative answer to this question. The two cases involving monocular vision gave clear-cut evidence of changes in both accommodation and convergence, and the binocular results certainly tend to supplement these findings. We cannot emphasize too strongly, therefore, that for our observers *the muscular efforts of accommodation and convergence were related to a subjective change of apparent distance with all other things remaining constant.*"

Discussion of accommodation and convergence

On the basis of the evidence discussed, certain conclusions can be drawn. Most immediately relevant is, of course, the general question of the conditions which are necessary to bring about a change in accommodation and convergence. That there is a definite and consistent pattern of muscular reactions involved in shifting from far to near vision is not subject to controversy. The fact that this pattern involving changes in accommodation, convergence, and pupillary contraction, described by Duke-Elder as the "near reflex," is elicited in every such shift is accepted by all writers, although there remains debate on the extent to which the three functions are independent of one another. However, as has been pointed out earlier, there is considerable question concerning the nature of the stimulus which brings about this "near reflex." Two possible answers have been suggested. One, characterized by "clearness," emphasizes the characteristics of the retinal patterns related to near and far objects, while the other, characterized by "nearness," stresses the role of apparent distance. The evidence would seem to indicate that these two factors are complexly interrelated. The fact that in normal vision we seem automatically to converge and accommodate upon the object of regard has led many writers to state that these functions are reflexly controlled. However, if apparent distance is a factor in determining ocular adjustment, as it has been shown to be, then the reflex concept must be greatly modified. A more correct statement of the general process would seem to call for (a) some aspect of the perceptual situation which will initiate a change in accommodation and convergence, and (b) an effort of these mechanisms until an adequate image is obtained. In normal everyday vision, the aspect of the perceptual situation which initiates ocular adjustment appears to be the subjective sense of the apparent distance of the object of regard.

Such a view cannot be incorporated within the classical view of accommodation and convergence. It can not be explained in terms of a simple spatial and temporal ordering of events—starting with the actual object, then to the optical properties of the light rays reaching the eyes, followed by automatic responses of the eyes appropriate to these optical properties, and eventually ending up with an apparent distance. The evidence is overwhelming that all these factors, and many others, are at once affecting and being affected by each other in a continuing process to which neither spatial nor temporal limits can be set. We can in no way consider accommodation and convergence as automatic responses of the organism to the environment, but rather as one of the results of a complex integrative process in which presumably each factor influences the ultimate outcome to the extent of the weight given it in terms of its past reliability as well as its present relationship to the inherited structure of the organism.

This approach to the "physiological cues" of accommodation and convergence is in line with what we have seen about the visual cues of space perception. It is impossible to speak of the visual cues as offered by the environment to the waiting organism. Rather they must be treated as abstractions created by the organism as it carries out its purposeful activity in an ever-changing relationship with its environment. This conclusion is in agreement with the more general conclusion that a visual perception, no matter how well structured, is not a disclosure of the external situation but rather a prediction made by the organism of what it is probably looking at. A perception is for purposeful action. The reliability of this prognosis will be related to the reliability and number of the indications or abstracted aspects whose integration constitutes the perception. Presumably, the relative reliability of these indications is learned from experience while carrying out purposeful activity.

The findings with respect to accommodation and convergence have an important application to this general theoretical picture. Emphasis has often been placed on the movements of the eye muscles as a principle underlying much, if not all, of the development of visual space perception. Explanations making use of this principle have, in general, not been successful simply because the actions that take place when accommodation and convergence are functioning are quite different from the actions involved in carrying out a purpose involving movement in space. The function of the activity of accommodation and convergence is solely to provide differentially characterized stimulus-patterns. These patterns are translated into perceptions that predict the probable significance of the environment and are used as directives for action. Thus, it seems evident that while one could learn the significance of space cues from action whose purpose involved behavior in a spatial environment, it would be much more difficult, if not impossible, to learn this from the action of the muscles related to accommodation and convergence. We may say that these mechanisms have served their purpose as long as they produce stimulus-patterns that are sufficiently differentiated to provide the related perceptual indications.

Part Three

SPECIAL PROBLEMS IN VISUAL SPACE PERCEPTION

IX

The Temporal
Course of Perception,
Perceptual Conflicts

THE TEMPORAL COURSE OF PERCEPTION

It is probably a truism that experience is somehow related to a temporally extended process in which both the real and the experienced "now" elude definition. It is nevertheless possible to break up experience into various stages, necessarily arbitrary, which succeed each other in definite temporal order, and to determine characteristic time durations for these various stages. Having done this, we can ask questions about the temporal order of events within any single stage. In the first part of this chapter we shall be concerned with the temporal sequences related to the "perceptual" stage of experience.

Every one of us has made a primitive experiment countless times: we first close our eyes and then open them. Two observations are consistently made. First, as soon as one opens one's eyes, one sees something. Second, what this something is depends upon what one happens to be looking at. These are facts of observation. They are related to two principles which have historically played an important role in psychological thought: one, the immediacy of perception, and two, the stimulus determination of perception. Immediacy as used in this context typically carries the double meaning of "without intermediary stages" and "instantaneous in time." The common-sense conclusion drawn from our simple experiment is that a perception is uniquely determined by the stimulus, that this perception is experienced simultaneously with the stimulation, and that the perception necessarily emerges in one fell swoop, without passing through any successive stages.

This view is manifestly naive, and thus stated it would be supported by very few theorists today. The argument of immediacy has tended to change into an argument of spontaneity, while that of stimulus-determination, as related to the problem at hand, has similarly changed into an argument of intransigence. That is, perceptions seem to arise spontaneously, and to resist change vigorously.

These arguments of spontaneity and intransigence probably sum up the thinking of many contemporary perception theorists. They derive primarily from the mistaken belief that something which occurs extremely quickly therefore occurs inevitably. One way of putting this assumption to experimental test is to study in detail the time interval between a change in impingement and the appearance of a changed stable perception. In order to define this time interval more specifically, it may be worthwhile to discuss the various stages into which the process can be broken up, as mentioned earlier.

Let us consider a hypothetical experiment. A light is turned on. When this is done, our subject turns it off by pressing a key. From the standpoint of an outside experimenter, we can roughly enumerate the sequence of events. The first stage is that of transit of the energy from the light source to the receptor, in this case the retina. There follows excitation of the peripheral receptor, then nerve transmission to various central areas. The next stage may, for the moment, be called central elaboration, which is followed by the appearance of an impulse along the efferent nerve which initiates motor activity which then alters the condition of the external light source. Characteristically, the time consumed in each of these stages is short. The total process may take as little as a quarter of a second or so, and the bulk of this time is undoubtedly consumed in the motor phase. The remaining stages probably have durations in the order of milliseconds or less. While, characteristically, these times are short, they are not necessarily so. For instance, if the stimulus is auditory and the source far distant, the transit time may be appreciable. The state of sensory adaptation may lengthen the excitation time considerably. If we tell our subject to press the key when he happens to feel like it, the period of central elaboration may extend to many seconds, minutes, or longer.

Nevertheless, it remains true that the time elapsed in the perceptual part of the sequence, defined here as the time between a change of impingement and the appearance of a changed stable perception, is characteristically extremely short. It is to this time interval that we shall devote our attention from here on. We want to point out, too, that by extremely short we mean extremely short relative to normal human functioning. The duration is very long indeed relative to high speed computing devices, for example. Nevertheless, for experimental purposes the order of a few milliseconds may be considered short. It has usually been assumed that this time can not be greatly extended. The chief tool for studying this part of the process has been the tachistoscope in which exposure times are used that are comparable to the duration of the process itself. Yet it remains desirable to approach the problem from the other direction, that is, to extend the duration of the process artificially into a length of time amenable to examination and study. It is desirable to do this for experimental reasons and because as long as one relies on tachistoscopic experiments, one is implicitly supporting the arguments of spontaneity and intransigence, the very arguments that much tachistoscopic work attempts to refute. If we can not, in the laboratory, extend the duration of the perceptual process beyond the few milliseconds commonly occupied, we can scarcely expect much credence to be given to our protestation that, nevertheless, in normal functioning outside of the laboratory this process is frequently temporally quite extended.

Fortunately, we have at our disposal several experimental techniques which do just this. The same general sequence of events can be observed in all the techniques.

First, the impingement on the retina is altered suddenly. Then, at some appreciable time later a changed stable perception is reported. The fact that this time interval is appreciable, sometimes being in the order of minutes, is in itself significant, and it offers us an opportunity for observing in detail the changes in perception over this period.

One such experiment will be described in some detail. An 8-foot cube, open on one side, and with the interior walls lined with leaves, can be viewed through the open side by an observer who is seated and who for this experiment is provided with a pair of Ames aniseikonic glasses. These glasses produce a change in the binocular disparity pattern—from that provided normally by the cubical room to the disparities which would be provided by some distorted, i.e., noncubical, room. At eye level along the back wall of the leaf room is placed a rod whose tilt can be controlled by the observer and automatically recorded as a function of time. At the start of the experiment, the observer is looking into the room, wearing no glasses or just his normal corrective lenses. He is told to set the rod so that it appears parallel, for example, to the ceiling of the room and to maintain the rod apparently parallel to the ceiling at all times. He is then given some practice adjusting the rod from various tilts. As soon as he is familiar with the apparatus, he again sets the rod apparently parallel to the ceiling, and the aniseikonic glasses are placed over his eyes. The apparent distortion of the room as a function of time can then be read directly from the recording of the position of the rod as a function of time.

Certain results are uniformly obtained with all observers. *First,* the room does not appear altered immediately after putting on the glasses. *Second,* some finite time later an alteration of the shape of the room is perceived. *Third,* this new apparent shape is not stable but continues gradually to change. *Fourth,* the room is perceived in a stable, altered shape. What are the time durations related to these various stages? The period of no apparent change

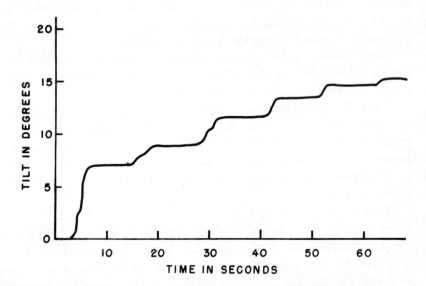

Figure IX-I   Apparent distortion of the "leaf room" as a function of time after putting on aniseikonic glasses.

varies from a minimum of one or two seconds up to as high as 30 seconds or even more. The duration between the first appearance of change in the shape of the room and the attainment of a final, stable apparent shape again varies widely from a minimum of two or three seconds up to commonly as long as two minutes or more. A typical curve of the position of the rod as a function of time is given in figure IX-1.

These results are easily and universally obtained both by the technique just described, as well as by others which will be described later. From these results we may draw some fairly definite conclusions. It is quite clear, first, that a finite time intervenes between a change of impingement and the appearance of a changed stable perception. Second, this time interval which is commonly quite short can experimentally be greatly extended for study. And third, the transition from one stable perception to another involves not only a finite time but also successive intermediary stages. In sum, it is possible for extensive and protracted changes of perception to take place over a period of time during which all sensory excitation remains constant and unchanging, and we have effective experimental techniques for studying such changes.

Perceptual lag

The fact that the perceptual process may be temporally quite extended is actually well established in the perception literature. It should be noted that although we have defined the "perceptual process" for the purposes of this chapter as the total process intervening between a change in impingement and the experience of a changed stable perception, we are primarily interested in the part of the process that occurs centrally. Since in the perceptual laboratory, external energies are most commonly altered, and excitation is rarely, if ever, altered, the definition offered provides a safer operational ground than would one which might attempt to restrict consideration to central processes. We are then concerned with cases of *perceptual lag*, defined as cases in which *perception changes over an appreciable period of time while impingement remains constant.*

It is apparent that this definition includes many cases which are not directly relevant to the purposes of this chapter but which will be noted for the sake of completeness. Sensory adaptation, for example, results in perceptual changes which fit into the operationally defined criteria for perceptual lag. Dark adaptation produces continuous changes in perception over periods as long as twenty minutes or more while the impinging energy remains constant. Equally fascinating are the regular changes occurring in afterimages, again without any change in external stimulation, first, from positive to negative fairly quickly, and then more slowly fading away. Perhaps less well understood but fitting into the same general category are the various after-effect phenomena which gradually wear away over time with attendant perceptual changes. Motion after-effect and figural after-effect, to cite two specific examples, both provide marked perceptual changes immediately following exposure to the critical stimulating situation, and these perceptual changes gradually decrease in magnitude over a fairly long period of time until they finally disappear completely.

While these examples formally fit the definition of perceptual lag as given, they will not be considered here since they depend either on well known peripheral physiological processes or on less well known central physiological or perceptual processes which are not directly relevant to the discussion at this point.

We will discuss another group of perceptual phenomena that offer the characteristic of continuously changing perceptions over long periods of time while impingement remains constant. A listing will introduce these phenomena.

a. *Reversible perspective effects* occur when there are two possible interpretations of the perspective of a single drawing. The well-known Necker cube is perhaps the most familiar example, but there are innumerable others equally persuasive. In all cases the effect perceived is an alternation between the two possible interpretations. In the Necker cube, first one face of the cube is seen in front and then, some time later, the other face is seen in front. This condition maintains for a period of time and then the reverse occurs. Characteristically, this alternation continues as long as the cube is being observed. Somewhat analogous effects are observable in ambiguous figure-ground situations in which first one part of the field emerges as figure and the other as ground with a subsequent reversal and alternation of the process.

b. The conditions of *binocular rivalry* are met when two appropriately dissimilar images are presented to the two eyes. Under proper conditions fusion does not occur, but, rather, first one image is seen, this gradually giving way to the other, which in turn gradually gives way to the first. There are many variations of this basic phenomenon, but the general characteristic of continual changes in perception, while the impinging energy remains unchanged, holds throughout them all.

c. In *centrifuge experiments,* the direction of gravitational force on the subject is altered and can produce marked perceptual changes. Under certain conditions, the perceptual changes do not become apparent until sometime after the direction of gravitational force has been changed as, for example, in the studies of Graybiel and his co-workers.

d. The *pseudoscope* offers an example of perceptual lag which was recognized and described by Wheatstone in his original article. The subject who looks at a scene or an object through the pseudoscope (which has the effect of reversing the positions of the two eyes optically) does not immediately perceive any change. Gradually, and sometimes over a considerable period of time, the appearance of the scene does change until it may take on the inverted characteristics induced by the pseudoscopic stimulation.

e. *Aniseikonic glasses* offer observations quite analogous to those of the pseudoscope. These glasses alter the binocular disparities in specific ways although not as drastically as the pseudoscope. We have already described the effects of these glasses when viewing the "leaf room." In general, the length of time between putting on the glasses and perceiving the apparent change in the objects of view is fairly extended.

f. The *monocular distorted rooms* provide situations which are physically of one shape, i.e., distorted, while apparently to monocular vision of another shape, i.e., normal. When one switches observation of one of these rooms from monocular to binocular or vice versa, appreciable time elapses before a changed perception is clearly evident. This effect is quite analogous to that of the aniseikonic glasses although it does not involve artificial optical alteration of the images.

g. *Long term adaptation* to distorting lenses, although not strictly fitting into the definition of perceptual lag, should be mentioned for completeness. It has been shown that the continuous wearing of distorting lenses, such as aniseikonic, prism or inverting lenses, for long periods of time produces marked changes in the perception of the same stimulus situation.

It is clear from this brief listing that a great deal can happen perceptually over long periods of time during which impingement remains unchanged. The listed cases offer an effective means for studying the temporal course of perception through greatly extending the usual time duration of the process. The inquiry is, however, only in its infancy. While its results will undoubtedly have importance not only for psychology but also for brain physiology, at the moment one can do little more than speculate.

The first question we must ask is what the conditions are under which this great extension of the temporal duration of the perceptual process can be observed. A general answer to this question is not yet possible. There are, however, two characteristics common to all the examples cited above which seem to be important. First, they all offer large, consistent and easily reproducible examples of perceptual lag, as earlier defined. Second, they all seem to involve the simultaneous presence of sets of conflicting cues. On the other hand, one notes immediately that there are at least two different kinds of observations indicated. Cases a) and b) involve continuous alternation between two different perceptions, while cases c) through g) involve regular sequences of change from one initial perception to another final perception.

Again, while conflicting cues are present in all examples, it is clear that these two groups of cases are different in the manner in which the cues are presented. In the first two examples, the conflicting cues are continuously present from the initial observation on, while in the remaining cases the conflict is introduced more or less suddenly subsequent to the initial viewing of the nonconflict situation.

While these are the general conditions for perceptual lag to occur, many others are also involved. There is evidence, for example, that the time involved is influenced by such factors as expectancy and immediately prior experience. Wide individual differences have been demonstrated in all cases. These individual differences may in part be related to differences in stereoscopic acuity and in eye dominance, to long term experiential effects, to the relative importance of the various cues involved, etc. Of equal interest is the possibility that there is a relationship between the duration of the perceptual lag and various personality factors. For example, there is evidence that something akin to rigidity may be involved as well as the stressful condition of the subject. These are hints which show that the process of perceptual lag is indeed a complex one, and that much investigation is still needed.

It is clear that one can no longer speak of the immediacy of perception, either in the sense of "without intermediary stages" or "instantaneous in time." To do so is to mistake the usual for the necessary. Rather, the temporal course of perception can properly be characterized as a continuous succession of changes all of which occur a finite time after impingement has changed, with each step of the process being affected by diverse factors. Furthermore, the duration of this process can be quite long.

PERCEPTUAL CONFLICTS

We now turn to a more generalized consideration growing out of the common condition characteristic of all the cases mentioned, namely, the presence of conflicting cues. Cues enter into any concrete transaction in combinations. An understanding of the visual space cues necessarily includes a study of these combinations. Taken in its greatest generality, this is, at our present state of knowledge, an impossibly complex problem. Everything said about the cues singly would have to be modified to a certain extent since every individual cue will be affected by the situation in which it is encountered. Any abstract general statements about the cues which do not take the existence of concrete conditions of observation into account are almost certain to be in error. As an example, some authors have attempted to rank the space cues in a hierarchy of importance, but have ignored the fact that the relative importance of the cues may very largely depend on the specific situations in which they are studied. The importance of a cue, in other words, is not a property inherent in the cue itself but rather an aspect of the way a specific individual utilizes that cue while he participates in a concrete transaction which includes many cues in complex combinations.

In an effort to reduce the complexity of cue combinations, we can, in keeping with most other writers on the subject, consider two different classes or types of cue combinations: those in which the cues are supplementing and those in which the cues are conflicting.

While this distinction is probably an artificial one which eludes rigorous definition, it is nevertheless a useful conceptual aid. Supplementing cues are those which taken singly lead to more or less similar or compatible perceptions, while conflicting cues individually lead to dissimilar or incompatible perceptions. Our attention will be limited to the latter situation.

Psychological conflict, whether perceptual or otherwise, represents one of the most important areas of psychological investigation. We have already dealt with this problem in its most general terms under the concept of "hitches," which were defined as situations in which "we do not experience a significance which we expected to experience." Hitches, it was further pointed out, "are always experienced in terms of the frustration of our purposes." A conflict situation can be thought of in this context as a kind of hitch in which the smooth onward course of behavior is interrupted by the simultaneous presence of two incompatible tendencies. From the standpoint of the participating individual such a condition introduces two important aspects which are probably not present under any other circumstances. In a conflict situation, the individual *chooses*, and he makes his choice with varying degrees of certainty or *surety*.

The extent to which the individual is aware either of choice or of surety depends on the specific conditions. If he experiences the existence of conflict, he is also aware of the necessity for choice and of the sense of surety which accompanies his choice. In many cases, however, the existence of the two incompatible alternatives is not experienced as such. The choice is unconsciously made, and the attendant sense of surety is associated with the actual outcome rather than with the process of choosing. In either event, choice and surety are intimately involved in any conflict situation. From the standpoint of the active participant, conflicts involve the process of evaluating and choosing between two or more potential courses of action. The study of conflicts, for this reason, can lead us into the study of such highly complex processes as value judgments and creativity. While these topics will not be dealt with here, they may ultimately turn out to be the major contributions that the study of perceptual conflicts can make.

On a more concrete level, many different kinds of conflicts have been studied by psychologists approaching the problem from a variety of directions. For example, learning theorists and similarly

oriented personality theorists have studied conflicts between incompatible responses. Psychoanalytically oriented theorists have
studied conflicts between dynamic forces operating within the
personality. Social psychologists have dealt with conflicts of loyalties, attitudes, group identifications, etc. Experimental psychologists
have studied conflicts in meaning, problem solving and a variety
of other special topics.

It is, of course, tempting to suggest that all such conflicts tap
similar underlying psychological processes, and that the study of
any one adds to the understanding of all. In a broad sense, very
likely this is so. Any general theory of psychological conflict, however, would be premature. The remainder of this chapter will be
limited to the specific question of perceptual conflict, or perhaps
more correctly, cue conflicts. Such a restriction does not in any way
deny broader implications. The generality derives from the fact
that perceptual conflicts, in a sense, lie at a junction from which one
can travel in two directions. Turning into the study of perceptual
processes, one can gain through the study of perceptual conflicts
an understanding of the dynamics underlying the problem of cues
in all possible combinations, both supplementing and conflicting.
Such questions as the relative importance of the various cues, the
factors which influence their importance, perceptual learning and
change, and intermodality combinations of cues can be clarified
through perceptual conflicts. Turning in the other direction, we
have seen that the concept of conflict occupies a major position in
other areas of psychology, notably learning theory and social, personality, and clinical psychology. The study of perceptual conflicts
offers a means for gaining new understanding of the processes involved in conflicts in these other areas.

Definition of conflict situation

According to the dictionary, conflict involves "the presence of
antagonistic tendencies." This is the way the term is usually used in
psychology, e.g., conflict of loyalties, conflict of responses, conflict of
cues. The implication of two warring camps, using the individual
for a battle ground but essentially not of him, is unfortunate. From
the standpoint of the individual actively participating in a concrete
transaction, what is involved is choice. In a conflict situation, as we
have seen, the individual chooses between incompatible alternatives.

For the purposes of this book, we can define a *perceptual conflict situation* as one which meets three criteria. First, two (or more) cues must be present. Second, each one of these cues if presented singly would result in a stable perception. Third, the two perceptions thus specified are mutually incompatible, i.e., they cannot be maintained at the same time. For example, we cannot see the same thing at two places at the same time. While this definition has obvious limitations, it is a working definition.

One of the immediate advantages of this definition is that it indicates specific directions along which study can proceed. Conflict situations, for example, can vary qualitatively, leading us to study the *nature of the conflict*. Or they can vary quantitatively, taking us into the question of the magnitude or *degree of conflict*. Different conditions can in turn be expected to lead to different outcomes, which forces us to consider the *modes of resolution* of conflicts and the *conditions favoring and inhibiting particular modes* of resolution. Enough is already known about these questions to warrant considering them in somewhat more detail although all conclusions in the study of perceptual conflict remain for the present tentative.

Nature of the conflict

A perceptual conflict situation has been described as one in which the several cues, if taken singly, would give rise to different and incompatible perceptions. The cues do not abstractly "fight" with each other. Rather it is the person who is faced with mutually exclusive ways of reacting. The precise nature of the incompatibility of the alternatives is not specified in this definition, and there is little direct experimental evidence to which one can turn. It seems clear, however, that the incompatibility can arise from various sources. For example, two alternatives may be "intrinsically" incompatible (one object cannot be two different colors at the same time or in two different places). Or the conflict may arise out of the denial of well established expectancies. There is, for example, nothing inherently incompatible in an object appearing to approach and get smaller at the same time, but such a situation is usually classified as introducing conflict because it goes counter to expectancy. Or a conflict in purposes may be involved. Many studies showing the influence of needs, values, etc., on perceptual processes may be considered as studies in perceptual conflict. It is, of course, possible and even likely that all these and other qualitative differences in the nature of the conflict situation may ultimately be reduced to some common principle, but for the present it seems profitable to treat them as separate cases.

Degree of conflict

The question of the magnitude or degree of conflict seems at first glance to offer fewer difficulties than does the specification of the nature of the conflict. The incompatibility between two alternatives is rarely an all-or-none proposition, and in most cases the alternatives offered can be arranged along a continuum from very nearly compatible to extremely incompatible. This can usefully be done, however, only if it is limited to one set of conditions at a time.

As a simple illustration, consider the case of two cues. One of the cues alone would lead to the perception of a particular object as being "far away," whereas the other cue alone would lead to the perception of the same object as being "nearby." Presumably, the degree of conflict can be related to the magnitude of the difference between these two apparent distances. The assumption here would be that there is a greater degree of conflict if the "far away" is a great deal farther away than if it is just a bit farther away—the greater the discrepancy the greater the conflict. This scheme for rating the magnitude of conflict seems straight-forward for that particular set of conditions. But how can this quantitative difference between degrees of conflict be related to the magnitude of the conflict when, let us say, one is presented with a red ace of spades? There is nothing inherently incompatible about a red ace of spades, but it goes contrary to all our experiences with playing cards. Is there a greater or lesser degree of conflict in a red ace of spades than in two cues which indicate the same object to be at two slightly different locations? At our present stage of knowledge the question is meaningless. We can only conclude that the degree of conflict is not a unitary concept but has different meanings depending on the nature of the conflict, the extent to which the two cues differ, the probabilities or degree of certainty assigned to each cue, the possibilities of reconciling them, and probably many other variables as well. Again, as in the case of the nature of the conflict, it may be that the concept of the magnitude or degree of conflict will ultimately be reduced to some common principle. But at the present the concept is most usefully considered as separately defined in terms of each specific situation which may be encountered.

Modes of resolution of conflicts

Every perceptual conflict must be resolved in some way. Whether this is true of all kinds of psychological conflict need not concern us here. There may be some conflicts which need not be resolved, the person presumably continuing "in conflict" for an indefinite period of time. It seems likely that close examination will prove such a statement to be meaningless under any conditions. Whatever an individual may do in a conflict situation must be considered as a mode of resolving that conflict. At any event, it is manifestly impossible for a perceptual conflict to continue without resolution. The only meaning such a statement could have would be "if no resolution, no perception." But even should such an unusual state occur, it would itself have to be considered a particular mode of resolution.

Perhaps it is because every perceptual conflict is in fact resolved in some way that the study of the modes of resolution has been more extensively pursued than any other aspect of perceptual conflict. The remainder of this chapter will be devoted to a more detailed discussion of the various kinds of resolutions which have been experimentally produced in perceptual conflict situations, with some discussion of the conditions under which they occur. No attempt is made to categorize the modes of resolution; they are merely listed. However, the resolutions can be made to fall into two very general classes which can be labeled disassociative resolutions and integrative resolutions. Some resolutions seem to move in the direction of minimizing the incompatibilities and mingling or integrating the various alternatives, while other resolutions proceed in the opposite direction, emphasizing the incompatibilities and pulling the alternatives still further apart so that they have little or no contact with each other. Whether such a distinction will prove to be fruitful remains to be seen.

Compromise resolutions. The resultant perception is neither one alternative nor the other but represents a compromise between the two. In the examples cited, the red ace of spades is seen neither red nor black but purple. The object is seen neither far away nor nearby but at some intermediate distance.

Compromise resolutions of perceptual conflicts represent the type most commonly referred to. Indeed, many writers seem to assume that this is the only form of resolution possible, an assumption which in part may be attributed to the fact that compromise is the most frequently observed and most easily produced of all conflict resolutions.

It is in the study of the constancies that we find the most frequent use of the concept of perceptual compromise, and it is here that the idea originated. Thouless advanced the general principle that "when two sets of sensory or perceptual cues which alone would give rise to phenomenal characters inconsistent with one another are presented together, the phenomenal character which is actually experienced is neither that indicated by one nor that indicated by the other set of cues but is a compromise between them."

Many other authors have pointed out, in many different terminologies, that in most constancy experiments the observed properties lie somewhere in between those predicted from one set of cues and those predicted from another set, both sets being simultaneously presented to the observer. Compromise resolutions have also been shown in the experimental juxtaposition of many isolated pairs of the various cues we have previously discussed. The procedure in all these cases is the same and offers a more rigorous operational definition of the compromise resolution than do the less well defined constancy experiments. Two cues are manipulated so that a single object on the basis of one of the cues alone is perceived at a grossly different location than on the basis of the other cue alone. When the two cues are presented together a compromise resolution is observed if the object appears at some intermediate point between these two locations.

Suppression resolutions. The resultant perception coincides with one of the presented alternatives. Within the limits of measurement the conflicting cue seems completely suppressed; its effects on the resulting perception are essentially zero.

The suppression resolution could be considered as a limiting case of compromise, but it seems qualitatively sufficiently different to be noted as a separate mode of resolution. This and the following modes of resolution have been far less extensively studied than has compromise, but there is sufficient evidence for certain conclusions. Suppression can be demonstrated if the two alternatives are either quantitatively extremely different or qualitatively incompatible.

As an illustration of quantitative differences resulting in suppression one can cite the distorted room of Ames. There are certain "give away cues" in the room which indicate its distorted shape, as has been shown by Kilpatrick, Wiener and others. These cues are typically suppressed and do not seem to affect the appearance of the room at all under the usual conditions of observation.

Qualitative incompatibility resulting in suppression can be seen when overlay is in conflict with other cues. If the other cues are dominant, the overlay is totally incompatible with the perceived situation and entirely ceases to function as a space cue, usually through a re-interpretation of the phenomenal properties of the object being viewed. In many cases, the suppressed cue loses its cue property through this re-interpretation. For example, brightness may be re-interpreted as a change in the external illumination; overlay appears as transparency; movement parallax becomes apparent physical movement of the objects being observed.

Temporal alternation as a resolution. Here the perception alternates between first one and then the other of two possible interpretations. This mode of resolution bears obvious similarities to suppression, and may represent the alternate suppression of first one cue and then the other. Once again, it seems qualitatively sufficiently distinctive to merit special inclusion. Although temporal alternation has been subjected to very little systematic experimentation, it seems clear that it can be observed under conditions in which the two cues are more or less equal in dominance while qualitatively not permitting a compromise resolution. Examples, which have been already cited, are reversible perspective and binocular rivalry.

Temporal delay as a conflict resolution. The perception slowly changes from one stable condition to another stable condition over a period of time. This we have already extensively treated in the case of the leaf room and the aniseikonic glasses.

Binocular-monocular conflicts—an illustrative case

Although there has been relatively little systematic experimental study of perceptual conflicts, the concept itself is by no means new in the study of visual space perception. It has perhaps most frequently been utilized in studying the relationship between binocular and monocular space cues. As early as 1852, Wheatstone, in discussing his pseudoscope, explicitly referred to the conflicts involved, "one idea being . . . suggested to the mind by one set of signs, and another totally incompatible idea by another set." The problem has been of recurring interest ever since. Ogle, for example, in 1959 refers to the fact that "in the usual surroundings encountered in ordinary life, the stereoscopic and empirical aspects of depth perception agree and aid each other." He later notes that "it is to be expected that in those surroundings that have been artificially produced to provide a conflict between stereoscopic stimuli and empirical factors, the meaningless stimuli may be suppressed by the meaningful, that is, by the perceptions from the empirical motives for depth."

In the years intervening between these two statements, many writers have referred to the conditions occurring in the binocular perception in a drawing or painting. Here the binocular indications of a flat surface are in conflict with the indications used by the artist to represent depth. Others have studied the ease of reversibility in the pseudoscope of a wide variety of objects. This question was systematically studied by Schriever who used drawings and photographs presented stereoscopically. By reversing right and left views, he was able to put selected monocular cues in conflict with binocular disparity and determine their relative effectiveness. He found superposition to be the most effective cue in overcoming the effect of disparity, while such indications as line perspective and shading were relatively ineffective. Ogle has similarly noted that "on the range finder the stereoscopic image of the reticules cannot be made to appear to recede through a building with details in spite of the uncrossed disparity introduced by the instrument."

An experimental approach to the study of the effect of conflicting size indications on binocular distance judgments was carried out by Vernon. He attempted to determine the effect of relative size differences in otherwise normal binocular observation. Two similar objects of different but constant visual angle were viewed binocularly and judgments were made as to their relative positions. Some confusion seemed to be introduced by the size conflict. The result was a slight reduction from the performance which would be predicted from complete reliance on binocular disparities. Other comparable studies (for example, those of Hirsch and his co-workers) have produced similar results, with either a very slight effect or no effect at all being introduced into normal binocular distance judgments by size differences. The situation seems to be quite different in the case of continuous size change, with the resultant appearance of movement either toward or away from the observer. The continuous size change seems to dominate the binocular disparities to a great extent. Under conditions optimally favoring the size cue, the introduction of binocular disparity has very little effect (Ittelson, W. Smith). Even under conditions optimally favoring disparity, continuous size change produces considerable apparent movement. This, of course, is the predominant cue producing the appearance of movement in motion pictures and television.

We have already referred to the use of the Ames aniseikonic glasses and the leaf room as a means for systematically studying binocular-monocular conflicts. Further discussion of this technique, together with a discussion of binocular rivalry as a conflict situation, will be found in the next chapter.

That the effects qualitatively described above are subject to systematic quantitative investigation is illustrated by two experiments of the author.

Experiment 1

Different degrees of compromise between monocular and binocular indications were achieved by varying the conditions of observation. The particular problem investigated arose from certain observations in the Ames distorted room. When this room is viewed monocularly the perception is of a rectangular room. When the room is viewed binocularly, its trapezoidal construction becomes evident. However, it is easily shown that this apparent trapezoidal shape does not correspond to the constructed trapezoid but represents a compromise between the monocular rectangular room and the trapezoidal construction one. The experiment presents an investigation of this observation.

The task given the subject was to adjust a variable comparison bar to the tilt of a fixed standard bar. The comparison bar rotated about a fixed horizontal axis placed at eye level to the subject and in the apparent center of the back wall of the distorted room. The standard bar coincided with the intersection of the back wall and the floor of the distorted room. This arrangement was viewed under the following five conditions.

1. Within the distorted room and viewed monocularly (DRM = distorted room monocular).

2. Within the distorted room and viewed binocularly. (DRB = distorted room binocular).

3. Removed from the distorted room and placed in a normal room with a homogeneous black background. All the spatial relationships between the observer, the comparison bar, and the standard bar remained exactly as in the distorted room. Viewed monocularly (NRM = normal room monocular).

4. Identical with 3, except viewed binocularly (NRB = normal room binocular).

5. The same as 4, except with the subject moved six feet farther away, thereby changing the monocular projection of the standard bar so that it was no longer horizontal (NRBD = normal room binocular distant).

This set of conditions represents a progression from optimum conditions for monocular indications to optimum conditions for binocular indications. Since the monocular projection of the standard bar was horizontal, tilting the comparison bar zero degrees would represent complete reliance on monocular cues, while a tilt of 14 degrees (representing the actual tilt of the standard bar) would be a correct setting representing a maximum reliance on binocular cues.

Figure IX-2 shows the mean settings for eight observers under the various conditions described. All points are significantly different from all others at better than the .05 level except for the comparison between NRM and NRB. It can be seen from Figure IX-2 that at one extreme there is almost complete reliance on the monocular cues, while at the other extreme there is almost complete reliance on the binocular cues, with different levels of compromise in between. (The figure for NRM indicates that perhaps this is an over-simplified view. A probably more correct interpretation is that binocular cues plus certain monocular cues of the correct tilt are in conflict with certain other monocular cues for the incorrect or horizontal tilt. The principle of compromise between two conflicting sets of cues, however, is not changed by this interpretation and the short-hand reference to binocular vs. monocular cues will be maintained with the understanding that the "binocular" cues probably include certain monocular ones as well.)

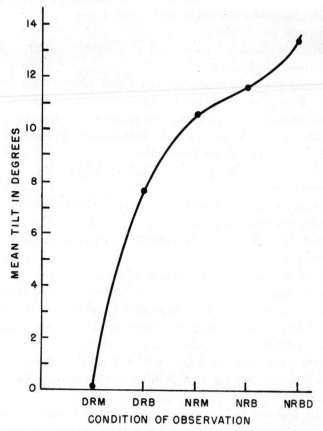

Figure IX-2 Resolution of a perceptual conflict situation as a function of conditions of observation.

It is possible to compute the relative weights given to the two sets of cues if we make the simple assumptions that, first, the apparent tilt is equal to the monocular tilt multiplied by the monocular weight plus the binocular tilt multiplied by the binocular weight and, second, that the sum of the monocular and binocular weights equals 1. These two statements are represented in the following two equations:

$$T = \text{apparent tilt} = MW_m + BW_b$$
$$W_m + W_b = 1$$

From these the monocular and binocular weights can be readily computed as follows:

$$W_m = \frac{T - B}{M - B}$$

$$W_b = \frac{T - M}{B - M}$$

Figure IX-3 shows the weights computed in this way for the varying viewing conditions.

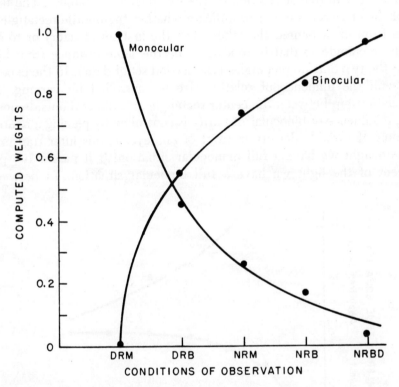

Figure IX-3   Relative weights given to monocular and binocular cues as a function of conditions of observation.

While the preceding experiment clearly demonstrates the possibility of quantitative variation in the degree of compromise between two sets of cues, it leaves much to be desired in the way of identification and control of the specific cues involved. In the following experiment this difficulty is largely eliminated. Binocular stereopsis and relative size are each systematically varied while all other cues are eliminated.

Experiment 2

The observer views three vertical illuminated rectangles in an otherwise completely dark room. The two outside rectangles are fixed while the center one can move toward or away from the observer. It is, furthermore, so constructed that in approaching and receding it maintains, from the viewpoint of the observer, a constant visual angle. The visual angle may be larger than, the same as, or smaller than that subtended by the two outside rectangles. The task of the observer is either to indicate whether the middle rectangle is in front of or behind the other two (the first set of data) or to set the rectangle so that it appears to be the same distance from him as the two outside rectangles (the second set of data). In the experiment, the influence of relative size is controlled by varying the relationship between the center rectangle and the two outside ones; the influence of binocular disparity is controlled by placing a neutral filter of variable density in front of one eye. If this filter transmits zero light we have a full monocular situation; if it passes 100 per cent of the light we have a full binocular situation. In between

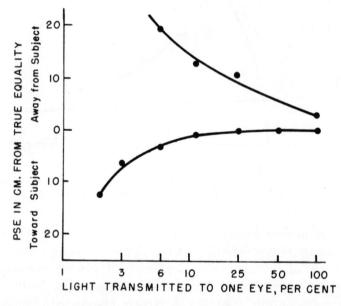

Figure IX-4 Resolution of binocular-monocular conflict as a function of the transmission of a neutral filter placed before one eye. The comparison stimulus subtended 8/7ths (upper curve) and 7/8ths (lower curve) of the visual angle of the standard.

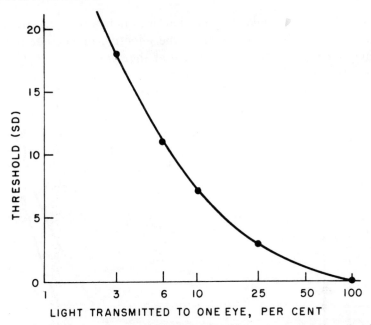

Figure IX-5   Difference threshold as a function of the transmission of a neutral filter placed before one eye.

it is possible to vary continuously from one extreme to the other. Other investigators have studied the effect of this condition on the horopter and stereoscopic thresholds, but these findings are not directly relevant and will not be discussed here.

In the first part of the experiment, two sizes of the center rectangle were used, 7/8ths of the visual angle of the outside rectangles, and 8/7ths of this angle. Seven values of filter were used in front of one eye, transmitting 1, 3, 6, 12, 25, 50 and 100 per cent of the light transmitted to the other eye. For each of these conditions a point of subjective quality and a threshold was determined by the method of constant stimuli. The results for two subjects are shown in Figures IX-4 and IX-5.

It is clear that reducing the illumination to one eye raises the binocular threshold when there are conflicting size cues. That it also reduces the weight given to the binocular stereoscopic cues in the resultant compromise is shown in Figure IX-4. As the illumination to one eye is progressively decreased, the point of subjective equality progressively moves in the direction indicated by the relative size cue until effective monocular perception is reached. (Since under these

conditions monocular observation does not permit determination of
a point of subjective equality, the effective monocular observation
may be considered to take place at that point beyond which it becomes impossible for the subject to report a point of subjective equality, indicated by the breaking off of the curves in the Figures.) It is
clear, then, that as the light transmitted to one eye is progressively

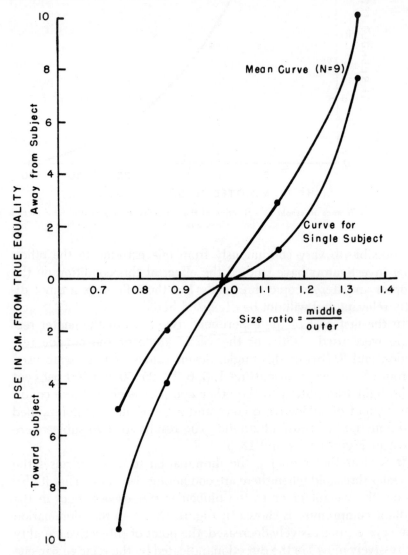

Figure IX-6   Resolution of a binocular-monocular conflict as a function of the ratio of visual
angles with a 10 percent transmission filter placed before one eye.

reduced, the weight given to the relative size cue is progressively increased.

In the second part of this experiment essentially the same procedure was followed except that the light ratio was maintained constant while the relative size ratio was systematically varied. The data were obtained in this instance by use of the method of average error.

Figure IX-6 shows the mean settings for nine subjects obtained under these conditions, together with a representative curve for a single subject. The slope of the curve shows the relative weights given to the two cues. A horizontal line indicates full weight given to the binocular cues and zero to the monocular, while a vertical line indicates no effect of the binocular and the full monocular cues. It is clear from an inspection of the curves that a point of inflection somewhere around a size ratio of unity represents an area of zero influence of the size cue. As the size ratios progressively vary from 1, the slope becomes greater until it eventually becomes asymptotic to the vertical axis, indicating that at these large size differences the influence of binocular stereopsis under these conditions has been reduced to zero.

It should be noted that these are representative curves. Great individual differences were observed under all conditions. For many observers effective monocular observation occurred at relatively small size ratios, while for others even at quite extreme size differences there was still a strong influence of binocular disparity. The curves shown represent the characteristic shape of the curves obtained for individuals.

In summary, one can state that this type of binocular-monocular conflict situation provides examples of all the known modes of resolution: compromise, suppression, temporal delay, temporal alternation. They all can be illustrated and studied quantitatively. In addition, there is a growing amount of information concerning the conditions necessary and sufficient for the appearance of each of these different modes of resolution.

Monocular-monocular conflicts

The monocular cues themselves may be placed in conflict with each other. This approach is more recent, and there is less systematic quantitative study.

The possibility of monocular-monocular conflicts was, for example, implied by Baird in his 1903 reply to Hillebrand. The latter had offered, as refuting the existence of an accommodation cue, the evidence that a diaphragm which grows smaller as it actually approaches the observer is seen as moving away. In his reply, Baird quite rightly pointed out that these results do not deny the existence of an accommodation cue but merely show the greater effect of the size cue. The phenomenon was not relevant to the problem at hand —"we are not concerned with the determination of the relative significance of the various criteria of distance." However, in dismissing the matter, Baird did not deny the importance of studies of the relative effectiveness of the visual cues and he hinted at a methodology.

Ames extended the use of perceptual conflicts to a large-scale study of the relative weights given the monocular depth cues. Following Ames' lead there have been many illustrations of conflicts between monocular cues, most of which have already been referred to under the discussion of the individual cues. Size-brightness conflicts, for example, usually result in either a compromise resolution or in a suppression of the brightness cue. Relative size has been placed in conflict with absolute or "familiar" size, with varying results (Ittelson, Ames, Hochberg). Under certain conditions a compromise resolution is reached; under others suppression of either one or the other cue can be shown, depending upon the specific circumstances. It is difficult at the present state of empirical knowledge to generalize the conditions under which one or the other cue will be dominant. In general, this statement applies with equal force to all other cases of monocular-monocular conflicts. Size-overlay, overlay-overlay, size-movement parallax, overlay-movement parallax, all provide evidence that the relative significance of one cue compared to another is a function primarily of the conditions under which the two cues are presented. Any cue can be made to dominate any other cue if the conditions are appropriate, and, therefore, the statement of relative cue importance becomes meaningless. The modes of resolution, however, which have been shown in monocular-monocular conflicts are in general identical with those earlier described.

X

The Perception of Persons
as Visual Objects

As in most relatively new fields, the subject matter in the study of person perception has not as yet been sharply defined, the problems have not been clearly delineated, nor has an adequate theory been formulated. In general, however, the kinds of problems studied have largely centered around feelings, attitudes, qualities, preferences, and the like, which one either perceives in the other person or experiences toward the other person, together with the determinants of these feelings, attitudes, etc. The underlying assumption in most of this work is that something the other person either *is* or *does* (i.e., his physical characteristics and his actions) provokes certain feelings in the observer as well as determines what feelings the observer will perceive the other person as having.

Yet, there is another side to the problem which has received far less attention. The physical characteristics and actions of the other person can affect the observer only as they are perceived. And these characteristics and actions, as perceived, may themselves be influenced by the observer's own attitudes, feelings, etc. We will now examine this aspect of the problem, namely, how the feelings and experiences of the observer influence the way in which he perceives the physical characteristics of the person—which is part of the more general question of the perception of persons as visual objects.

Our question is not something apart from the more common problems of person perception. Rather it is a central point around which these problems must be organized. In practice, it has most frequently been by-passed by assuming, usually tacitly, the accuracy of the perception of the object characteristics of the other person, and assuming further that a theory of person perception can be developed on this foundation. With this assumption, the study of person perception does itself a two-fold injustice.

First, such an assumption denies to person perception the benefits of all the recent work on the important role of familiarity and emotional factors in the recognition and perception of object properties. Certainly, person perception cannot afford to take the paradoxical position of assuming that these effects do not occur in the very area where one might reasonably expect them to be most important, since persons, of all stimuli, are most consistently familiar and most deeply loaded with affective implication.

Second, by making this assumption, person perception is not recognizing its own potential for contributing to an understanding of the problems of object perception. There is no justification for assuming that object perception stands in any sense logically or functionally prior to person perception. Such an assumption necessarily introduces distortions.

A familiar example from person perception will illustrate this. We know that if A likes B he will also, in general, experience B as liking him (or at worst as being indifferent to him). The case of A liking B when he believes B to dislike him almost never occurs. However, when we ask B how he feels about A, we find that A is frequently mistaken. That is, A experiences B as liking him when in fact B dislikes him. If we examine this case, two possible alternatives emerge. Either B is fooling A, or A is fooling himself. If B is deliberately fooling A for social or ulterior motives then there is no problem, A is merely the dupe of B. But we can assume that, at least part of the time, A is misperceiving B.

The essential point is that A's like of B depends on his perception of B's like of him, at the same time that his perception of B's like of him depends on his like of B. This example presents a paradox if we make the assumption that one process must occur prior to the other. The paradox disappears and a reasonable approach to the problem becomes possible if we recognize that both processes occur simultaneously and inter-relate with each other.

A similar apparent paradox occurs in the study of object perception. The assumption is frequently made that one cannot recognize an object until one has perceived its metric (or dimensional and shape) properties. This seems logical enough, until one realizes that in some cases the opposite holds true—when the perception of metric properties depends on recognition of the object, either as a specific object or at least as a member of a particular class of objects. We can no more safely say that perception of metric properties comes prior to recognition than we can say the opposite. Both processes occur simultaneously and inter-relatedly.

The problems inherent in approaching perception in an hierarchical manner, in which one process is given precedence over another, have been chosen as an illustrative example. Let us now turn to a more detailed consideration of some important theoretical issues which are raised when one includes persons in the class of stimuli studied as visual objects.

SOME THEORETICAL ISSUES

We shall briefly recall some ways in which visual objects have been studied and, in doing this, consider one type of experiment as a paradigm to keep in mind. Our take-off point is the size-constancy experiment as pioneered by Holway and Boring and as repeated in one variation or another many times since. In this experiment, stimuli of different sizes are placed at various distances as "standards," and psychophysical methods, especially the method of reproduction, are used to get metric judgments of size, or perhaps distance, on a comparison stimulus. One set of parameters in this experiment is the number and variety of physically controlled cues or clues to size and distance which are allowed to the subject in the making of his judgment. We may vary the number, type or combination of any of the cues already discussed, as well as the distances, sizes, type of objects, instructions, method of responding, etc.

We wish to refer to the Holway-Boring experiment in general as a set of methodological limits or as a model or paradigm, rather than as a particular study with a particular set of variables. We will also need to make reference to recognition experiments and phenomenological reports, although the paradigms for these need not be stated here.

First, we will consider the objects which have been used in these studies, thinking of them, now, as belonging to a larger class of objects which *might be* studied by such techniques. With few exceptions, these objects have been considered as neutral, that is, devoid of meaning, emotional content and other implications not reasonably translatable into the response dimensions which are allowed the subject. They are supposed to be objects without subjective connotations—"objective" objects. Actually they are figures of simple geometry (circles, squares) or sticks made of wood or cardboard or holes in something illuminated from behind. One might think that such objects are far removed from persons and that data from such objects would have little bearing on the data obtained from, say, studies of the affective relations between people. Also, one might think that an understanding of affective relations between people would contribute nothing to an understanding of perceptions of such objects.

However, a second thought leads us to realize that most objects we can think of, and certainly the geometrical figures that have been used as stimuli, can be considered to have a personal significance in the sense that they *imply* human beings in their existence in space and time. To all intents and purposes geometrical figures do not just "occur" in nature, they are *made* by people. These objects are artifacts in the same sense that the "meaningful" objects are artifacts, and are no doubt recognizable to our subjects as things made by experimenters for certain purposes. They differ from other objects not because of the absence of meaningful implications but because of the variety and generality of the implications. A circle, for example, could imply a much larger number of things than a wedding band, but both a circle and a wedding band imply persons.

It might be possible to list objects in some kind of order according to how related they are to persons in general and in particular. Real people, including the perceiver himself as an object of his own view, would certainly come at one end of the list and unfamiliar objects assumed to have very little to do with people, like the other side of the moon, would be at the other end. Artifacts, objects made by a known person, objects made by oneself, representations of people, and representations of loved ones would go in the middle. We don't know whether this is a continuum in every sense of the word, or whether the positions would remain invariant across different types of responses, but at least we can see that the class of objects which can be studied is much larger than that which has been studied, and we can say some things about the objects which might influence the perception of their metric properties.

It is very likely, for example, that there are differences between familiar and unfamiliar objects in the metric perceptual responses to them; or that there would be differences in recognition and in apparent size and shape between, say, representations of people and real people; that these differences show up despite the fact that we control for other cues; and that they will show up even in the restricted, special and often functionally inappropriate kinds of responses which we, for one methodological reason or another, force our subjects to make.

Except that one set of objects is easier to make or to vary experimentally than another, there is no reason why we should select it. Expediency is hardly an adequate rationale. Why have the geometrical figures been so emphasized? Perhaps because experimenters had a suspicion that "something else" enters the picture as the object becomes more "meaningful."

Consider, for example, repeating the Holway-Boring experiment with live human beings in place of the geometrical figures. What would happen? Technically, this experiment would be extremely difficult since Holway and Boring controlled for visual angle, which would mean that we would have to vary the size of a human being. However, if it could be done we would predict that the people would all be seen as 5-6 feet tall and at the appropriate distance independent of how big they really were or how far away. Of course, we can conceive of our subject saying, "He really looks 20 feet tall," but we cannot conceive of our subject saying, "He really is 20 feet tall." He would probably be speechless and emotionally upset. Remember, we are talking here about *real* people as objects because the experience of reality on the part of the subject is a condition for best results in this hypothetical experiment. Although this ideal experiment can not be done, we can approach it in some ways, and we can make some predictions on the basis of evidence already collected as to the factors which are important in the perception of metric properties of persons and in the recognition of persons.

The distorted room of Ames provides us with some evidence as to the tenacity with which we hold on to our assumptions regarding the metric properties of persons as we think they really are as opposed to what we see. In this demonstration we are presented with almost all the cues necessary for us to see a person double in height before our eyes.

A room is constructed in such a way that, although one rear

corner is twice as far away as the other one, both corners appear at the same distance in between their real distances. The room appears absolutely normal. As our real person walks from one corner to another, the room as a field is still seen as normal since there are an overwhelming number of the familiar indications that this is an ordinary room with all lines normal (perpendicular) to all planes. What happens is that the person appears to get larger and smaller. We become upset, laugh or cry, we feel we cannot trust our senses, we become angry at the people responsible, we say, "It's all a trick, it's done with mirrors," or try to rationalize. But we never give up the idea that the person is "really" unchanging in height. One experience of this sort is not enough to make us change our assumption about the real stability of the size and shape of people. And why should it? Although there are great perceptual conflicts going on with emotional concomitants, and although the illusion is very near perfect cue-wise and the *apparent* size of a real live person is changing phenomenally, our highly valued assumptions about the nature of the physical properties of people do *not* change. Were the experimenter to see only the response data gathered from "bet" or "reality" instructions ("Tell me how large you think the object really is if we were to measure it with a ruler") he would conclude that nothing unusual was happening.

On the other hand, Kilpatrick has shown that with manipulative experience in the distorted room subjects can quite quickly come to respond that the room is *really* distorted and only after long term experience that it *appears* to be distorted. Why these apparently contradictory results, in one case with rooms and in the other case with people? The answer is, in part at any rate, that the subject assumes that although things may be done with rooms as constructed objects, people are not constructed and cannot be made to change in their metric properties. The subject is, of course, correct in this assumption.

The late comedian Fred Allen described a vaudeville performer who could appear to grow a few inches. There may be a few other instances of such things. But, overwhelmingly, our assumptions about the constancy in the metrics of persons (over short periods of time) are founded upon a wealth of highly regular evidence from our experience. Statues and other representations of people which provide almost the same visual cues as do real people do come in various sizes and do not provide us with the same constancy of experience. For this reason, we would expect differences in the perception of the metric properties of an object, depending on whether the perceiver assumes it to be a real person and on the surety attached to that assumption.

An analysis of these illustrations provides us with two groups of characteristics which show promise of having importance for our understanding of the visual perception of people. These characteristics cannot be said to be independent; they are hard to separate operationally, and they can never be shown to be anything other than useful abstractions with which we can summarize some aspects of a process. They are *familiarity* and *emotional loading*. We might call them *object familiarity* and *object cathexis* except for the fact that it is absurd to imply that they are properties of objects. Likewise they are not purely properties of the perceiver. Both the object and the subject are necessary for the definition of these characteristics in any concrete case; they are characteristics of the relationship which exists between subject and object.

It is proposed that—no matter what the results from other research, such as word recognition, perception of objects, picture perception—the perception of the size, shape, and distance of objects which are really experienced as real people will be affected by these two factors. To be concrete, we are suggesting that the perception of the metrics of one's mother will be different from an unknown person and from an equally known but less loved person, as these objects (persons) are made to vary in size, shape, and distance.

This is not to say that familiarity and emotional loading do not affect our perception of squares and circles; indeed they may, but we have not much more familiarity with, nor libido invested in, one square than another. For this reason, and perhaps for this reason alone, it is hard to show effects of these factors when we use geometrical figures. The same may hold for symbols, words, and pictures as objects of recognition.

There is a point to be made here about the relevance of results obtained with one set of objects for results with another set of objects. If emotionality and familiarity can be shown to influence recognition or metric properties of a set of objects, they will probably have equal or greater influence with objects nearer to persons on the previously mentioned list of object types. The reverse is not the case. Just because emotionality cannot be shown to influence recognition and metrics of a group of objects does *not* mean that it will not have an influence with objects higher on the list. Thus, although the influence of emotionality on the recognition times of pictures may be a second-order effect, it may well be a primary factor in the recognition of real people.

With regard to the influence of these factors on "neutral" objects, it must be considered that squares and circles do not come in all sizes in our experience, nor do lines and other figures of this sort. The findings reported in Chapter V on size-distance perception of unfamiliar objects show that even our neutral objects have sub-jective assumptions about them which influence the perception of their metric characteristics. It is also probable that we have emo-tional investments in certain characteristics of geometrical figures. When a figure which looks like an oscillating rectangle can be shown to be really a rotating trapezoid we become anxious until we gain understanding of the process involved. In general it can be said that we have an emotional investment in the stability of certain proper-ties of things, and that when our expectancies are violated we feel anxious. If the discrepancies between our assumptions and the con-sequences of our actions are great enough and unaccountable enough and persistent enough, severe emotional disturbance may re-sult. Similarly, continued wearing of distorting lenses has been found to produce emotional depression and withdrawal.

These factors of familiarity and emotional loading may well be latent and of little consequence in some perceptual studies of non-living objects or objects relatively unrelated to living beings, but when we begin to deal with persons as objects of view we come face to face with their importance. One of the most striking exam-ples of the influence of familiarity on the perception of shape is to be found in the face matrix of Wheatstone. The inside of a mask from very few feet away and viewed binocularly, looks like the outside of the mask. A face viewed through a pseudoscope, such that the left eye receives the image normally given to the right eye and vice versa, looks like a normal face. This inside-out illusion is so striking and gives an impression so strong that it is almost impos-sible *under any circumstances* for all parts to appear as one would predict from disparities. That is, the face continues to look normal under this complete reversal of the binocular cues. The human face may have some properties of a good Gestalt, but Gestalt theory seems inadequate to account for the fact that an irregular or asymmetrical face looks more real than a face made perfectly symmetrical by substituting a mirror image for one real half, or for the fact that much about a face (even a pretty one) is not "closed" or "good figure," etc. Except for the circularity of the pupils of the eye, there are no simple geometrical figures in a real face. Many compelling perceptual properties of the human face can most reasonably be attributed to experience.

These conclusions are foreign to theorists who build theories on the basic assumption that the perceptual process is something like a "chain" of events which do not change their order. Thus perception in some sense is primary, and must come before states and responses (like emotion) which are dependent on it. Stimulus must precede response. Perception is basic to familiarity, but familiarity is not basic to perception, etc. The perceptual process is considered as a sequence of events leading from stimulus through to response, with transformations along the way which cause many changes but which do not alter the priority of events. Under this point of view perception of the metric properties of objects has a special priority. Somehow, it must be immediate to the stimulus, and must precede other processes, such as recognition, cognition, judgment, memory and emotion. Perception thus takes over the role of *sensation* of the old schools as the process most immediate to, and dependent upon, the external physical stimulus.

As we have seen, this view is inadequate in the light of modern findings. Neurological evidence is beginning to show the existence of many feedback systems where we never expected them. If the system is a chain it is one where a process occurring at one point in the chain is affected by processes occurring further up in the chain. It is *not* a matter of what happens at a point in time being affected by something happening later in time. The actual time for "information" to travel through the system is very short compared to our response and stimulus times. When we reduce our stimulus and response times we do not decrease the mutual influence of these factors, if anything we increase their influence. So-called "projective" effects come dramatically into play when stimulus times are decreased. When response latencies are decreased the effects of set and familiarity are increased. It becomes a matter of all processes affecting one another and being interrelated in many ways. The way we study such a system depends upon what we are trying to study about it, and our choice of variables will greatly influence our results.

If we instruct a subject to make a metric response and prevent him from doing other things, we cannot assume that we are tapping just a certain part of his system, or that what we are tapping has any priority over other parts. The restricted responses which our subjects make are quite conceivably expressions of more factors than are "reasonable" under the instructions and are therefore inadequate to represent, distinctly, all that is happening. Thus our subjects are perceiving more than and less than they are "supposed to" under a strict interpretation of the instructions. Making the responses simple does not make perception simple, and complex responses bring new variables into play. All of us know that we can instruct our subjects, if we really try, to be influenced by emotionality and familiarity. When we try to instruct them *not* to be so influenced we may find ourselves in the dilemma of the man who was trying not to think of the word "rhinoceros."

We are not suggesting that these factors are response artifacts; quite the contrary, they are inseparable parts of a process and they will influence our variables depending on how we study that process.

All psychologists agree that familiarity affects recognition, although they may express it in different ways. What has only recently been proved is that familiarity affects the perception of the metric properties of objects, both in the presence of and in the absence of conflicting cues. In Chapter V it was pointed out that familiarity can operate as the sole cue to size and distance, as well as being effective even in the presence of a full complement of other conflicting indications. These studies have been done with simple familiar objects, such as playing cards and chairs. The technique consists in presenting the objects to the subject in *other* than their familiar size and noting regression of responses toward the subjective size expectancy, as compared to various control objects which do not have strong familiar size implications.

The familiar objects of constant experienced size derive their real invariance of size from their functional relationships to the dimensions of human beings—a chair is always the size it is because the bottoms of people are always the size they are, etc. If this relationship has any bearing on perceived size, then the perceived metric properties of persons and other objects would be influenced by the assumptions on the part of the subject of the size of people. With regard to the influence of familiarity on shape constancy we shall have more to say later. That there is an influence is undoubtable, and here again the findings are that a person is the example par excellence of a familiar object, and hence distorts less readily than anything else.

Since persons have the characteristic of being highly emotionally loaded or valued and highly familiar, it is hard to know which of these factors is contributing most to the data obtained in recent investigations. This brings us again to the general problem of the effects of emotional factors on recognition and metric perception. Although the studies of the influence of emotional factors on word and object recognition leave us still somewhat with an open mind, it looks as though much of the data can be accounted for on the basis of familiarity alone. This finding cannot be generalized to make predictions about the results we would obtain in studies with human beings.

To summarize relevant aspects of the work to date, we can say:

1. Familiarity has a major effect on the recognition of all objects including people, and, indeed, it would be paradoxical if it did not.

2. Familiarity has a major effect on the perception of metric properties of shape, size, and distance of all objects including people.

3. There is some evidence from studies of objects other than people that emotional loading has a minor effect on recognition, but we cannot say the effect will be minor when studies are done with people.

4. The evidence using other objects is somewhat ambiguous at the moment, but there is some new evidence on the influence of emotional loading on the perception of metric properties of people which we will discuss in the next section.

Familiarity and emotional loading are not unrelated variables and are difficult to consider separately, and even more difficult of translation into distinct experimental operations. However, some new techniques show promise for distinguishing the influence of these factors.

SOME EMPIRICAL FINDINGS

Discussion of specific experimental findings concerning the perception of persons as visual objects will be limited to three different experimental approaches. The first, using aniseikonic lenses, has to do with the apparent distortion of the metric proportion of persons. The second deals with the study of person perception using the method of binocular rivalry developed by Engel. The third approach studies the apparent size-distance relationships of photographs of persons, utilizing the Ames "Thereness-Thatness" apparatus. We will first outline the findings of each approach separately and then summarize the conclusions common to all three.

Perception of persons using aniseikonic glasses

When an observer wearing a pair of aniseikonic glasses views any object, two interesting optical effects occur. First, the binocular disparities are altered in a particular way depending upon the particular lenses used and, second, nothing else of any significance occurs. An understanding of the effects produced by aniseikonic glasses depends on an understanding of both these points.

First, when wearing these glasses, an observer receives binocular disparities which are not those which he would receive were he viewing the same object without glasses, but which instead are those he would receive from some other hypothetical object were he viewing that object without glasses. The exact properties of this second, hypothetical object can be computed from a knowledge of the glasses, along the lines indicated in Chapter VII. For example, without the glasses, an observer viewing a plane surface perpendicular to his line of sight receives the disparities appropriate to such a surface and, indeed, sees a plane surface perpendicular to his line of sight. He now puts on a particular pair of aniseikonic glasses and receives disparities appropriate to a plane surface tilted 45 degrees to his line of sight. The two conditions, (1) glasses viewing actual perpendicular surface and (2) no glasses viewing hypothetical tilted surface, are equivalent as far as binocular disparities are concerned. If binocular disparities are the sole or primary determinant, one would expect the observer to see a tilted surface, and this is indeed what occurs under appropriate conditions.

However, we must bear in mind the second effect of the aniseikonic glasses: while the disparities are changed, nothing else happens. The monocular images remain effectively unchanged. This is possible because the binocular disparity thresholds are so small compared to monocular thresholds that important binocular changes can be introduced without even approaching monocular thresholds.

Thus, when an observer wearing aniseikonic glasses looks at an object, he is receiving binocular disparities from some different, hypothetical object as well as all monocular cues from the object he is actually viewing. In short, wearing the aniseikonic glasses introduces a marked binocular-monocular conflict as discussed in the preceding Chapter.

We have described these effects in some detail because they offer us a type of conflict situation which can be used to study the effect of familiarity and emotional loading. We have binocular disparities indicating a distorted object and monocular cues indicating a non-distorted or normal object; we can weigh the monocular cues through familiarity and emotional loading and study the effect on the distortion.

Of course, we already have one general finding from the face matrix (or pseudoscopic) data, and from the distorted room evidence. Persons do not readily appear distorted. Going beyond this general finding, we can compare the relative amounts of apparent distortions as an observer views persons in varying relationships to himself. The conditions in these studies are essentially the same. The subject, wearing aniseikonic glasses, views one or more persons under standardized conditions, and measures are obtained of the apparent distortion of the person he is viewing. Briefly, the kinds of relationships studied and the major findings of a series of experiments by Wittreich were:

1. Subject viewing marital partner as compared to stranger. The marital partner was reported as appearing less distorted than the stranger.

2. Subject viewing authority figure as compared to peer. This study was conducted using Navy "boot" trainees as subjects viewing a fellow "boot" and a petty officer. The authority figure was reported as appearing less distorted than the peer.

3. Subject viewing an amputee as compared to a normal person (i.e., nonamputee), both strangers to the subject. The results indicated that the amputee appeared less distorted than the normal.

One general finding runs through all of these studies. When an observer views another person through the aniseikonic glasses, the perceived distortion is inversely related to the significance of the relationship between the two persons. Or, in other words, important people do not appear to distort as much as unimportant people. The words "significant" and "important" are deliberately used here because they are ambiguous. Exactly what the determining features of the relationship are is not clear. In some cases (e.g., marital partner) familiarity is confounded with emotional loading, while in others (e.g., amputees) familiarity seems to be either equated or even in the opposite direction. Again, with respect to emotional loading, both positive and negative affect seem to give the same overall result. From another point of view, one can point out that in all cases studied the observer had a greater investment in the stability of the person appearing to him less distorted. Might not the opposite effects occur if one could find a relationship in which the investment was in change rather than stability?

Such speculation points out opportunities for further research in this area that would uncover in detail the relevant aspects of the interpersonal relationship. The basic finding remains that, under these conditions, the apparent metric properties of another person depend on the relationship between that person and the one who is viewing him.

Person perception under conditions of binocular rivalry

The phenomenon of binocular rivalry has long been known to experimental psychologists. Within the past four or five years this venerable topic has been revitalized by the exciting work of Engel as an important technique for the study of emotional processes in perception and particularly person perception.

In the typical binocular rivalry experiment an image is presented to one eye of the subject, and another image, different in some way from the first, is presented to the other eye. This is most conveniently done using some form of the stereoscope. Under these conditions several possible perceptual alternatives can occur, depending at least in part on the nature and magnitude of the differences between the two images. One relatively trivial case may be mentioned. If the two images occupy completely different parts of the field, a single image is seen which is simply a combination of the two separate images. Two more important observations are commonly made: (1) If the differences are not too great, a single stable image is observed. This is the condition of binocular fusion. (2) If the differences are sufficiently great, first, one image in its entirety is observed; this gradually blends into the second, until ultimately the second image alone is seen, only to have the process then reversed—in a steady alternation between the two images. This is the condition of binocular rivalry.

The problem of binocular fusion has been extensively and continuously studied. Not so, however, the question of rivalry. Occasionally an investigator has devoted himself to a study of the usual geometric stimuli, and this work has resulted in a few generalizations about the formal geometric properties of these stimuli which are related to greater or lesser rivalry effects. Against this historical background, Engel asked what would be the effect, in a typical rivalry experiment, of using stimuli which were more heavily weighted with respect to familiarity and emotionality. For this purpose he chose persons as stimulus objects, using both photographs and real live people.

Let us examine the conditions under which the results were obtained. The observer views a photograph of a person with one eye, and with the other eye he simultaneously views a photograph of a person which differs in some way from the first. Under these conditions, it is already established that the observer has several possible perceptual alternatives: he can have fused images, combined images, or alternating images. We have here again a conflict situation in which the observer is faced with two or more mutually exclusive alternatives. The effect of familiarity or emotional loading will be demonstrated if one or another of these alternatives is weighted more heavily so that that alternative is reported more frequently or more readily than would be the case with so-called neutral stimuli. In addition, there remains the possibility, which as we shall see was actually realized under certain conditions, that the use of this class of objects may introduce new alternatives not previously observed.

It should also be noted that an important advantage of this technique is that the observer is typically completely unaware that he himself is producing the perceptual effects he is observing. Even under conditions of maximum alternation, the naive observer believes that he is passively observing a stimulus which is actually being varied by the experimenter.

We will outline some of the more interesting findings of what an observer sees when faced with these various possible ways of perceiving two different photographs, one presented to each eye.

1. Composite face

In this case a photograph of a face is presented to one eye and a similar photograph of a different face is presented to the other. The basic finding is that a single stable face is perceived; the subject is invariably unaware that he is doing anything other than looking at a picture of a face. Furthermore, this mode of perceiving seems to have characteristics which are different from those previously reported as possible resolutions of the rivalry situation. The perceived face is neither a fusion nor a combination of the two presented faces. For this reason, Engel has termed it a composite face.

Interesting variants of this basic experiment have been performed.

Two male faces. The perceived composite face is almost invariably reported as being not just another face but rather an "ideal" face in some sense, being more handsome and finer in character than either of the two presented faces when they are viewed singly.

One male-one female face. In this case, the typical report (far from being of an ideal face) is of either a masculine-looking woman or an effeminate man.

Self and unknown face. In many cases the observer does not recognize his own face as entering into the composite. Beloff and Beloff found that the composite containing the unrecognized self is rated more positively than is a composite made up of two strangers.

Gradual introduction of second face. If the illumination of one face is initially zero and is then gradually increased, the subject frequently reports the apparent face as unchanging, even up to the point when the illumination of the two faces has become equal. In extreme cases, the first face may then be gradually darkened, still without the subject reporting any change in the apparent face.

2. Suppression of one image

In some instances, offering quite different pictures to the two eyes, a single stable image is perceived which is simply one of the two presented pictures, the other being entirely missing. Two conditions under which this effect occurs have been reported.

Inverted face. Two similar faces are presented one to each eye, with one being upright and the other inverted. The typical report is simply the upright face. Occasionally a partial combination image is reported with one or two parts of the inverted face intruding themselves onto the upright face. The original finding by Engel was repeated by Hastorf and Myro using upright and inverted postage stamps.

Face-genital presentation. Here a representation of a male face was presented to one eye and a representation of male genitals to the other eye. Again, the alternation expected in the usual rivalry situation does not occur. Most frequently simply the male face is seen, occasionally parts of the other figure appear as extraneous and un-recognized additions. In the rare instances in which the face disappears and the genital figure appears in its entirety, it is ordinarily not recognized initially.

It is evident from these studies that the modes of resolution obtained in a binocular rivalry experiment, using photographs of persons as stimuli, are in many cases different from those obtained using geometric stimuli, and that one cannot be predicted directly from the other. Specifically, the resolution has been shown to depend on both familiarity and emotional loading. In the inverted face experiment, the effect is clearly one of familiarity. With the composite face, emotional or motivational factors seem predominant. The face-genital conflict presents an excellent example of the difficulty of separating familiarity, emotionality, and structural properties. Much more work is needed before we will understand all the factors involved together with the relationship between them, and this work is being pursued. It is clear that the use of persons as stimuli opens new dimensions in the study of binocular rivalry, and, conversely, binocular rivalry provides us with an important and exciting technique for studying person perception. Further work can rest on the solid evidence that, when persons are used as stimuli, the particular resolution achieved in the binocular rivalry situation is determined, in part at least, by factors of familiarity and emotional loading.

Person perception using photographs in the Ames "Thereness-Thatness" apparatus

In these studies we turn to a reduced cue situation, in contrast to the use of conflicts represented by the previous two groups of studies. Using reduced cues enables us to show the effect of the particular aspects under consideration, in this case familiarity and emotional loading, by reducing in so far as possible all other sources of variability. Effects which might be masked in a more complex situation are thereby brought clearly into focus. The reduced cue technique is ideally suited for showing if a particular effect exists and for studying its details in isolation.

The Ames "Thereness-Thatness" apparatus was chosen for the studies. Using this apparatus we can study the effect of emotionality, for example, on the apparent distance at which an object is perceived. In a typical experiment, the subject may set an emotionally loaded object to appear at a particular distance, and the experimenter examines this setting to see if the fact of emotionality has influenced it.

Let us see how this is accomplished. The apparatus consists of two separate visual fields stretching straight ahead of the subject for 12-15 feet. The fields are separate, that is, from the standpoint of the experimenter. They are physically separated and independently controlled. From the standpoint of the subject, however, these two combine, and for him there is only one visual field, which he sees straight ahead, starting perhaps a foot or two in front of him, running off into the distance and ending in blackness. Leaving the subject for a moment, let us examine the two fields of the apparatus. One of these, the comparison field, is essentially our distance measuring device, our yardstick. The aim of this field is to provide a situation as close to the normal or usual as is possible under the necessarily restricted condition of the experiment, so that apparent distances within this field will be comparable to apparent distances of everyday life. To accomplish this, the comparison field is viewed binocularly and such cues as relative size, perspective, etc., are provided. In practice this field usually consists of a row of posts of constant size, in a straight line parallel to the observer's median plane. Distance judgments can reliably and accurately be made under these conditions, and it is relative to this comparison field that the apparent distance of an object in the second, experimental, field is judged. The experimental field is simplicity itself. It consists of a single object, the particular stimulus under investigation, suspended, disembodied, against an otherwise completely black background, and viewed with one eye. This object can be moved back and forth along a path extending in a straight line from the observer and parallel to the row of posts. Since the experimental object is a single object viewed monocularly, presumably the only important cue to its distance is provided by some assumption of its absolute size which the subject makes without being aware of doing so. That this is indeed the case has been amply borne out by the findings cited in Chapter V.

With this in mind, we may return to the subject. He sees a row of posts stretching out ahead of him and an object which he can move to and fro, parallel to the posts. His task may be, for example, to set this object at the same distance from him as a particular post designated by the experimenter. The subject typically performs this task readily, without question and without difficulty although not without boredom after a few such settings have been made. He does this completely unaware of the facts (1) that he is performing the rather remarkable feat of projecting a subjective estimate of the actual size of the stimulus object, (2) that he is making his distance settings on the basis of this projected or assumed size, and (3) that the experimenter from the distance settings can make inferences concerning this projected size and the influence of such characteristics of the stimulus object as its familiarity and emotionality.

The role of familiarity under these conditions has been discussed in Chapter V. We are here concerned with the effect of emotionality, studied by using as stimulus objects photographs of persons in various affective relationships to the subject. The experimental conditions for all the studies are essentially the same. The subject is presented with a series of photographs, one at a time, and is asked to make distance settings of these photographs relative to the comparison posts. Assuming proper controls for structural properties of the photographs, any differences in the setting of one photograph from the next must be attributed to differences in the emotional loading of the photograph, presumably operating through differences in the projected or assumed size of the photographs. We will now summarize the results of such studies.

1. *Using posed photographs of pleasant and unpleasant faces.*

G. H. Smith has reported a series of these studies involving a number of interesting variations. His basic finding was a difference in the settings of faces rated pleasant as compared with those of faces rated unpleasant.

2. *Children viewing photographs of themselves and other children.* This study gave negative results as a developmental study. No trends with age were found. However, of interest is the finding of a slight but consistent tendency for all ages to set the self-picture differently from the pictures of other children.

The studies 1 and 2 use as a measure the actual distance in inches from the eye of the observer to the setting of the photograph. While the results are positive in that they show the influence of emotional loading, this measure has two drawbacks. First, the comparatively small effects due to emotionality tend to be masked by such larger effects as the subjects' idiosyncratic tendencies to set all things near or all things far. Second, one can not necessarily assume that emotionality will produce effects in the same direction for all subjects. If it should turn out that subjects react to emotional loading in different ways, then these may tend to cancel each other out, unless the measure used specifically takes into account the direction as well as the magnitude of the effect. The following three studies overcame both of these problems, by using as a measure the setting of the photographs relative to the setting of a neutral familiar object. This eliminates general size-distance tendencies (which will show themselves in the neutral object as well) and takes into account the direction of the effect (which shows with reference to the neutral object). That is, the measure used was the magnitude and direction of the difference between the settings of the photographs being studied. In all cases the statement, "a difference was found between the setting of an emotional and of a neutral photograph," is to be interpreted as meaning: if the neutral photograph was set farther than the control object, then the emotional photograph was set still farther, while if the neutral photograph was set closer than the control object, then the emotional photograph was set still closer. This point is stressed because this idiosyncratic direction effect is of both technical and theoretical interest.

3. *Self picture with normal subject.* Each subject made settings of a self photograph and a photograph of a stranger. The self was set significantly differently from the stranger.

4. *Group therapy study.*   Each patient in a therapy group made settings of a photograph of each of the following persons:

That other member of the group whom the subject most liked, in the opinion of the two therapists of the group.

That other member of the group whom the subject least liked, in the opinion of the two therapists.

The two therapists.

Himself.

Significantly different settings were obtained between the self and least liked, and the most liked and least liked.

5. *Psychiatric ward study.*   Sociometric measures were obtained from patients on a psychiatric ward, and each patient subsequently made settings of photographs of himself and other patients selected on the basis of the sociometric data. The results again show significant effects for the self-picture, and suggest that both highly liked and highly disliked persons are equivalent on this task and are both different from relatively neutral persons.

One general conclusion can be drawn from the studies. The apparent metric properties of photographs of persons, as measured in this experimental situation, are influenced by the affective relationship between the subject and the person photographed. Beyond this statement we can make some further tentative conclusions and point out questions for study. Exactly what the important aspects of the affective relationship are again remains unclear. Furthermore, subjects seem to differ in the direction of the effect, and increasing the magnitude of the emotional loading increases the effect in the direction peculiar to that subject. Subjects who tend to set all emotionally loaded objects farther than relatively neutral objects will tend to set heavily loaded objects still farther than less loaded objects. In other subjects, the entire effect is reversed. One can speculate as to whether this may not represent basic differences in personality structure and ways of dealing with the world. Again, it is significant that all the effects observed are greatest when we are dealing with photographs of the self. Surely this suggests the possibility of an experimental approach to the problems of the self-image.

REFERENCES

REFERENCES

Ames, A., Jr. *An interpretative manual for the demonstrations in the psychology research center.* Princeton: Princeton Univ. Press, 1955

Ames, A., Jr. Binocular vision as affected by relations between uniocular stimulus patterns in commonplace environments. *Amer. J. Psychol.,* 1946, *59,* 333-357

Ames, A., Jr. Reconsideration of the origin and nature of perception. In Ratner, S. (ed.), *Vision and action.* New Brunswick: Rutgers Univ. Press, 1953

Ames, A., Jr. Sensations, their nature and origin. *Transformation,* 1950, *1,* 11-12

Ames, A., Jr. Some demonstrations concerned with the origin and nature of our sensations (what we experience). A laboratory manual (preliminary draft). Hanover, N. H.: Hanover Institute, 1946 (mimeographed)

Ames, A., Jr. Visual perception and the rotating trapezoidal window. *Psychol. Monogr.,* 1951, *65,* No. 324

Ames, A., Jr., and Gliddon, G. Ocular measurements. *Trans. Sec. Ophthal. Amer. Med. Ass.,* 1928 (June 15), 1-68

Baird, J. W. The influence of accommodation and convergence upon the perception of depth. *Amer. J. Psychol.,* 1903, *14,* 150-200

Bappert, J. Neue Untersuchungen zum Problem des Verhältnisses von Akkommodation und Konvergenz zur Wahrnehmung der Tiefe. *Zeitschrift Psychol.,* 1923, *90,* 167-203

Bartley, S. H. *Beginning experimental psychology.* New York: McGraw-Hill, 1950

Bartley, S. H. *Vision, a study of its basis.* New York: Van Nostrand, 1941

Beloff, J., and Beloff, H. Perception of self and others using stereoscope. *J. abn. soc. Psychol.,* 1959, *56*

Bentley, Arthur F. The fiction of "retinal image." In Ratner, S. (ed.), *Inquiry into inquiries: Essays in social theory.* Boston: Beacon Press, 1957

Blank, A. A. The Luneburg theory of binocular space perception. In Koch, S. (ed.), *Psychology: A study of a science,* Vol. 1. New York: McGraw-Hill, 1959

Boring, E. G. *A history of experimental psychology.* New York: Appleton-Century, 1950

Boring, E. G. *Sensation and perception in the history of experimental psychology.* New York: Appleton-Century, 1942

Boring, E. G., Langfeld, H., and Weld, W. *Foundations of psychology.* New York: Wiley, 1948

Bourdon, B. *La perception visuelle de l'espace.* Paris: Schleicher Freres, 1902

Brewster, Sir David. *The stereoscope, its history, theory, and construction,* 1856

Bridgman, P. W. Science and common sense. *Scientific Monthly,* 1954 (July), 32-39

Brunswik, E. *Systematic and representative design of psychological experiments.* Berkeley: Univ. Calif. Press, 1947

Calavrezo, C. Über den Einfluss von Grössenänderungen auf die scheinbare Tiefe. *Psychol. Forsch.,* 1934, *19,* 311-365

Cantril, H., Ames, A., Jr., Hastorf, A. H., and Ittelson, W. H. Psychology and scientific research. *Science,* 1949, *110,* 461-464, 491-497, 517-522

Cantril, H. Ethical relativity from the transactional point of view. *J. Philo.,* 1955, *12,* 677-687

Cantril, H. Perception and interpersonal relations. *Amer. J. Psychiat.,* 1957, *114,* 119-126

Carr, H. A. *An introduction to space perception.* New York: Longmans, Green, 1935

Chapanis, A., and McCleary, R. A. Interposition as a cue for the perception of relative distance. *J. Gen. Psychol.,* 1953, *48,* 113-132

Clark, W. C., Smith, A. H., and Rabe, A. Retinal gradient of outline as a stimulus for slant. *Can. J. Psychol.,* 1955, 9, 247-253

Dewey, John, and Bentley, Arthur F. *Knowing and the known,* Boston: Beacon Press, 1949

Donders, F. C. *Accommodation and refraction of the eye.* (Trans. by W. D. Moore) London: New Sydenham Society, 1864

Duke-Elder, Sir W. S. *Textbook of ophthalmology.* 4 vols. London: Kimpton, 1932-1949

Duncan. As reported in Carr, H. A., *An introduction to space perception.* New York: Longmans, Green, 1935

Eissler, K. Die Gestaltkonstanz der Sehdinge bei Variation der Objekte und ihrer Einwirkungsweise auf den Wahrnehmenden. *Arch. ges. Psychol.,* 1933, *88,* 487-550

Engel, E. Binocular fusion of dissimilar figures. *J. Psychol.,* 1958, *46,* 53-57

Engel, E. Binocular methods in psychological research. In F. P. Kilpatrick (ed.), *Explorations in transactional psychology.* New York: New York University Press, 1960

Engel, E. Meaningful content in the study of rivalry and fusion: Preliminary observations. (Progress memorandum, Psychology Research Center). Princeton: Princeton Univ., 1955 (mimeographed)

Engel, E. The role of content in binocular resolution. *Amer. J. Psychol.,* 1956, *69,* 87-91

Fry, G. A. Comments on Luneburg's analysis of binocular vision. *Amer. J. Optom.,* 1952, *29,* 3-11

Fry, G. A. The relationship between geometrical perspective and stereo cues. *Amer. J. Optom.*, 1952, *29*, 353-368

Fry, G. A. Visual perception of space. *Amer. J. Optom.*, 1950 (Nov.), Monog. 110

Gibson, J. J. *The perception of the visual world*. Boston: Houghton Mifflin, 1950

Graham, C. H. Visual perception. In Stevens, S. S., *Handbook of experimental psychology*. New York: Wiley, 1951

Graham, C. H., Baker, K. E., Hecht, M., and Lloyd, V. V. Factors influencing thresholds for monocular movement parallax. *J. exp. Psychol.*, 1948, *38*, 205-223

Grant, V. W. Accommodation and convergence in visual space perception. *J. exp. Psychol.*, 1942, *31*, 89-104

Graybiel, A., and Brown, R. H. The delay in visual reorientation following exposure to a change in direction of resultant force on a human centrifuge. *J. gen. Psychol.*, 1951, *45*, 143-150

Gruber, H. The relation of perceived size to perceived distance. *Amer. J. Psychol.*, 1954, *67*, 411-426

Hahn, E. L., and Bartley, S. H. The apparent orientation of a luminous figure in darkness. *Am. J. Psychol.*, 1954, *67*, 500-508

Hardy, L. H., Rand, G., and Rittler, M. C. Investigation of visual space. *Arch. Ophthal.*, 1951, *45*, 53

Hardy, L. H., Rand, G., Rittler, M. C., Blank, A. A., and Boeder, P. *The geometry of binocular space perception*. New York: Knapp Memorial Laboratories, Inst. Ophthalmol., Columbia Univ., Coll. Physic. Surg., 1953

Hastorf, A. H. The influence of suggestion on the relationship between stimulus size and perceived distance. *J. Psychol.*, 1950, *29*, 195-217

Hastorf, A. H., and Myro, G. The effect of meaning on binocular rivalry. *Amer. J. Psychol.*, 1959, *72*, 393-400

Hastorf, A. H., and Way, K. S. Apparent size with and without distance cues. *J. gen. Psychol.*, 1952, *47*, 181-188

Helmholtz, H. *Physiological optics*. (Trans. by J. P. C. Southall) Opt. Soc. Amer., 1925

Helson, H., and King, S. M. The tau effect: an example of psychological relativity. *J. exp. Psychol.*, 1931, *14*, 202-217

Hering, E. *Spatial sense and movements of the eye*. (Trans. C. A. Radde) Baltimore: Amer. Acad. Optom., 1942

Hillebrand, F. Das Verhältnis von Accommodation und Konvergenz zur Tiefenlokalisation. *Zsch. F. Psychol., u. Physiol. d. Sinnesorg.*, 1894, *7*, 77-151

Hirsch, M. J., Horowitz, M. W., and Weymouth, F. W. Distance discrimination: III. Effect of rod width on threshold. *Arch. Ophthal.*, 1948, *39*, 325-332

Hochberg, C. B., and Hochberg, J. E. Familiar size and the perception of depth. *J. Psychol.*, 1952, *34*, 107-114

Hochberg. C. B., and Hochberg, J. E. Familiar size and subception in perceived depth. *J. Psychol.*, 1953, *36*, 341-345

Hofstetter, H. W. The proximal factor in accommodation and convergence. *Amer. J. Optom.*, 1942, *19*, 67-76

Holway, A. H., and Boring, E. G. Determinants of apparent visual size with distance variant. *Amer. J. Psychol.*, 1941, *54*, 21-37

Ittelson, W. H. *The Ames demonstrations in perception.* Princeton: Princeton Univ. Press, 1952

Ittelson, W. H. The constancies in perceptual theory. *Psychol. Rev.*, 1951, *58*, 285-294

Ittelson, W. H. Size as a cue to distance: Radial motion. *Amer. J. Psychol.*, 1951, *64*, 188-292

Ittelson, W. H. Size as a cue to distance: Static localization. *Amer. J. Psychol.*, 1951, *64*, 54-67

Ittelson, W. H., and Ames, A., Jr. Accommodation, convergence and their relation to apparent distance. *J. Psychol.*, 1950, *30*, 43-67

Ittelson, W. H., and Cantril, H. *Perception: A transactional approach.* New York: Random House, 1954

Ittelson, W. H., and Slack, C. W. The perception of persons as visual objects. In Tagiuri, R., and Petrullo, L. (eds.), *Person perception and interpersonal behavior.* Stanford: Stanford Univ. Press, 1958

Jastrow, J. Critique of psychophysic methods. *Amer. J. Psychol.*, 1888, *1*, 271-309

Johns, E. H., and Sumner, F. C. Relation of the brightness differences of colors to their apparent distances. *J. Psychol.*, 1948, *26*, 25-29

Kilpatrick, F. P. (ed.) *Human behavior from the transactional point of view.* Princeton: Institute for Associated Research, 1952

Kilpatrick, F. P. Two processes in perceptual learning. *J. exp. Psychol.*, 1954, *47*, 362-370

Kilpatrick, F. P., and Ittelson, W. H. The size-distance invariance hypothesis. *Psychol. Rev.*, 1953, *60*, 223-231

Kilpatrick, F. P., and Ittelson, W. H. Three demonstrations involving the visual perception of movement. *J. exp. Psychol.*, 1951, *42*, 394-402

Langdon, J. Further studies in the perception of a changing shape. *Quart. J. exp. Psychol.*, 1953, *5*, 89-107

Langdon, J. The perception of a changing shape. *Quart. J. exp. Psychol.*, 1951, *3*, 157-165

Langdon, J. The perception of three dimensional solids. *Quart. J. exp. Psychol.*, 1955, *7*, 133-146

Langdon, J. The role of spatial stimuli in the perception of shape. Part I. *Quart. J. exp. Psychol.*, 1955, *7*, 19-27

Langdon, J. The role of spatial stimuli in the perception of shape. Part II. *Quart. J. exp. Psychol.*, 1955, *7*, 28-36

Lawrence, M. *Studies in human behavior.* Princeton: Princeton Univ. Press, 1949

LeGrand, Y. Etudes binoculaires. II. La théorie de l'espace visuel de Luneburg. *Att. d. Fond. Giorg. Ronchi*, 1954, *9*, 44-51

Leventhal, Morton. Color as a variable in perceptual response. A study of depth perception and word recognition in schizophrenic and other psychiatric patients. Unpublished Ph.D. thesis. Univ. of Kansas, 1953

Linksz, A. *Physiology of the eye.* New York: Grune and Stratton, 1952, Vol. I

Luckiesh, M., and Moss. F., *The science of seeing.* New York: Van Nostrand, 1937

Luneburg, R. K. *Mathematical analysis of binocular vision.* Princeton: Princeton Univ. Press, 1947

Luneburg, R. K. The metric of binocular space. *J. Optical Soc. Amer.*, 1950, *40*, 627-642

Luneburg, R. K. Metric methods in binocular visual perception. In *Courant Anniversary Volume.* New York: New York University Press, 1948

Metzger, W. Tiefenerscheinungen in optischen Bewegungsfeldern. *Psychol. Forsch.*, 1934, *20*, 195-260

Miller, J. W., and Bartley, S. H. A study of object shape as influenced by instrumental magnification. *J. gen. Psychol.*, 1954, *50*, 141-146

Morgan, M. W. The clinical aspects of accommodation and convergence. *Amer. J. Optom.*, 1944, *21*, 185-195, 301-313

Munster, C. Über den Einfluss von Helligkeitsunterschieden in beiden Augen auf die stereoskopische Wahrnehmung. *Zschr. Sinnesphysiol.*, 1941, *69*, 245-260

Nelson, T. M., and Bartley, S. H. The perception of form in an unstructured field. *J. gen. Psychol.*, 1956, *54*, 57-63

Ohwaki, S. On the factors determining accommodation: Research on size constancy phenomena. *Tohaku Psychol. Folia*, 1955, *14*, 147-158

Ohwaki, S. The role of accommodation in the size constancy phenomenon. *Tohaku Psychol. Folia*, 1954, *14*, 17-31

Ogle, K. N. *Binocular vision.* Philadelphia: Saunders, 1950

Ogle, K. N. Theory of stereoscopic vision. In Koch, S. (ed.), *Psychology: A study of a science*, Vol. I. New York: McGraw-Hill, 1959

Peter, R. Untersuchungen über die Beziehungen zwischen primären und sekundären Faktoren der Tiefenwahrnehmung. *Arch. f. d. ges. Psychol.*, 1915, *34*, 515-564

Petermann, B. Über die Bedeutung der Auffassungsbedingungen für die Tiefen und Raumwahrnehmung, *Arch. f. d. ges. Psychol.*, 1924, *46*, 351-416

Pouillard, G. Contribution a l'étude expérimentale de la notion spatiale de la profondeur. *J. Psychol. Norm. and Path.*, 1933, *30*, 887-929

Pratt, C. C. The role of past experience in visual perception. *J. Psychol.*, 1950, *30*, 85-107

Ratoosh, P. On interposition as a cue for the perception of distance. *Proc. nat. Acad. Sci.*, 1949, *35*, 257-259

Sanford, E. C. *A course in experimental psychology.* Boston: Heath, 1901

Schilder, Paul. *Medical psychology.* New York: International University Press, 1953

Schlosberg, H. A note on depth perception, size constancy, and related topics. *Psychol. Rev.,* 1950, *57,* 314-317

Schriever, W. Experimentelle Studien über stereoskopisches Sehen. *Zeitschrift Psychol.,* 1925, *96,* 113-170

Sheehan, M. R. A study of individual consistency in phenomenal constancy. *Arch. Psychol.,* 1938, 31, No. 22

Slack, C. W. Familiar size as a cue to size in the presence of conflicting cues. *J. exper. Psychol.,* 1956, *52,* 194-198

Slack, C. W. Feedback theory and the reflex arc concept. *Psychol. Rev.,* 1955, *62,* 263-267

Smith, G. H. Size-distance judgments of human faces (projected images). *J. gen. Psychol.,* 1953, *49,* 45-64

Smith, G. H. Size-distance settings as indicative of personal adjustment. *J. soc. Psychol.,* 1954, *40,* 165-172

Smith, W. M. Effect of monocular and binocular vision, brightness, and apparent size on the sensitivity to apparent movement in depth. *J. exp. Psychol.,* 1955, *49,* 357-362

Smith, W. M. Past experience and perception: A study of the influence of past experience on apparent size and distance. Ph.D. thesis. Princeton Univ., 1950

Smith, W. M. Past experience and perception of visual size. *Amer. J. Psychol.,* 1953, *65,* 389-403

Smith, W. M. Sensitivity to apparent movement in depth as a function of "property of movement." *J. exp. Psychol.,* 1951, *42,* 143-152

Smith, W. M. Sensitivity to apparent movement in depth as a function of stimulus dimensionality. *J. exp. Psychol.,* 1952, *43,* 149-155

Stavrianos, B. K. The relation of shape perception to explicit judgments of inclination. *Arch. Psychol.,* 1945, No. 296

Stevens, S. S. Mathematics, measurement, and psychophysics. In Stevens, S. S., *Handbook of experimental psychology.* New York: Wiley, 1951

Thouless, R. H. Individual differences in phenomenal regression. *Brit. J. Psychol.,* 1932, *22,* 216-241

Thouless, R. H. Phenomenal regression to the real object. *Brit. J. Psychol.,* 1931, *21,* 339-359

Toch, H. H. The perceptual elaboration of stroboscopic presentations. *Amer. J. Psychol.,* 1956, *69,* 345-358

Toch, H. H., and Ittelson, W. H. The role of past experience in apparent movement: A revaluation. *Brit. J. Psychol.,* 1956, *47,* Part 3, 195-207

Tschermak-Seysenegg, A. V. *Physiological optics.* (Trans. by P. Boeder) Springfield: Chas. Thomas, 1952

Vernon, M. D. *A further study of visual perception.* Cambridge: Cambridge Univ. Press, 1954

Vernon, M. D. The perception of distance. *Brit. J. Psychol.,* 1937, *28,* 1-11

Vernon, M. D. *Visual perception*. Cambridge: Cambridge Univ. Press, 1937

von Kries. In Helmholtz, H. von., *Physiological optics*. (Trans. by J. P. C. Southall) Optical Society of America, 1924

Wallach, H. Brightness constancy and the nature of achromatic colors. *J. exper. Psychol.*, 1948, *38*, 310-324

Wallach, H., and O'Connell, D. N. Kinetic depth effect. *J. exp. Psychol.*, 1953, *45*, 205-217

Wallach, H., and O'Connell, D. N. The memory effect of visual perception of three-dimensional form. *J. exp. Psychol.*, 1953, *45*, 360-368

Walls, G. L. *The vertebrate eye*. Bloomfield Hills, Mich.: Cranbrook Instit. Sci., 1942

Weiner, M. Perceptual development in a distorted room: A phenomenological study. *Psychol. Monog.*, 1956, *70*, Whole No. 423

Wheatstone, C. On some remarkable, and hitherto unobserved phenomena of binocular vision, Part I. *Lond. R. Soc. Philos. Trans.*, 1838, 371-394

Wheatstone, C. On some remarkable, and hitherto unobserved phenomena of binocular vision, Part II. *Philos. Mag. Series*, 1852, *4(3)*, 504-523

Whitehead, A. N. *Dialogues of Alfred North Whitehead*. Compiled by Lucien Price. Boston: Little, Brown, 1954

Whitehead, A. N. *The principles of natural knowledge*. Cambridge: Cambridge Univ. Press, 1925

Whitehead, A. N., *Science and the modern world*. New York: Macmillan, 1925

Witkin, H. A. Perception of body position and of the position of the visual field. *Psychol. Monogr.*, 1949, No. 302

Wittreich, W. J. The Honi phenomenon: A case of selective perceptual distortion. *J. abn. soc. Psychol.*, 1952, *47*, 705-712

Wittreich, W. J. The influence of simulated mutilation upon the perception of the human figure. *J. abn. soc. Psychol.*, 1955, *51*, 493-495

Wittreich, W. J. Visual perception and personality. *Scientific American*, 1959, *200*, 56-60

Wittreich, W. J., and Radcliffe, K. S., Jr. Differences in the perception of an authority figure and a non-authority figure by navy recruits. *J. abn. soc. Psychol.*, 1956, *53*, 383-384

Woodworth, R., and Schlosberg, H. *Experimental psychology*. New York: Henry Holt, 1954

Zegers, R. T. Monocular movement parallax thresholds as functions of field size, field position, and speed of stimulus movement. *J. Psychol.*, 1948, *26*, 477-498

INDEX

CONNECTICUT COLLEGE LIBRARY
152.6 lt7
Visual space perception.

dc

3 1839 001537988